RE:BUILD

A VIDEO COURSE & WORKBOOK DESIGNED TO GIVE PRACTICAL GUIDANCE AND FACILITATE CRUCIAL CONVERSATIONS TO REBUILD TRUST

BY JASON B. MARTINKUS & THOMAS A. BERRY

A REDEMPTIVE LIVING PRODUCTION

COPYRIGHT NOTICE

TABLE OF CONTENTS

WELCOME TO REBUIILD : A VIDEO COURSE AND WORKBOOK BASED ON THE BEST SELLING BOOK *WORTHY OF HER TRUST*

Thank you for joining us! It is an honor to provide content to help you navigate the messy, absolutely not formulaic process of healing and rebuilding trust after sexual betrayal.

Frankly, we wish this were not a part of your story and you and your family were spared the heartache and devastation that results from sexual betrayal. There is, however, hope to rebuild trust, gain intimacy and connection through radical honesty, empathy, and integrity. Our desire in creating this study is to provide guidance and tools to help you navigate the journey and hopefully avoid pitfalls and setbacks that can slow down the healing process.

We believe, because of our own experiences, that Redemptive Living is not just a ministry...it's a possibility for all marriages. Our hope is this course helps you toward that end.

WELCOME

HOW IT WORKS

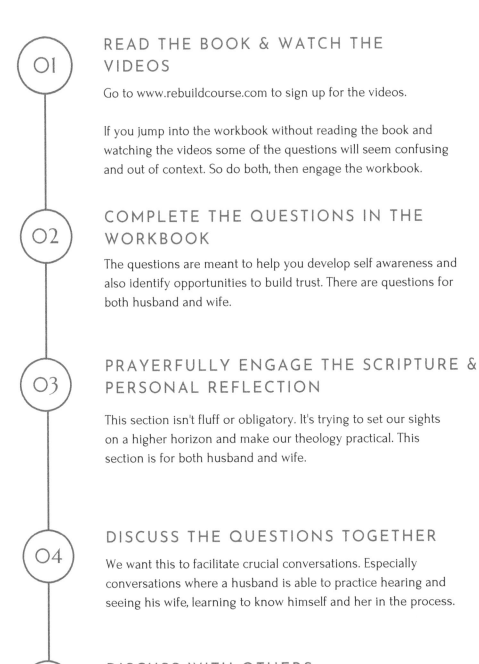

01 READ THE BOOK & WATCH THE VIDEOS

Go to www.rebuildcourse.com to sign up for the videos.

If you jump into the workbook without reading the book and watching the videos some of the questions will seem confusing and out of context. So do both, then engage the workbook.

02 COMPLETE THE QUESTIONS IN THE WORKBOOK

The questions are meant to help you develop self awareness and also identify opportunities to build trust. There are questions for both husband and wife.

03 PRAYERFULLY ENGAGE THE SCRIPTURE & PERSONAL REFLECTION

This section isn't fluff or obligatory. It's trying to set our sights on a higher horizon and make our theology practical. This section is for both husband and wife.

04 DISCUSS THE QUESTIONS TOGETHER

We want this to facilitate crucial conversations. Especially conversations where a husband is able to practice hearing and seeing his wife, learning to know himself and her in the process.

05 DISCUSS WITH OTHERS

We're fans of community; being with like-minded people to support us. Whether working through this in a group or individually, we encourage you to share your work and what you are learning with a supportive person/people.

LEADERS GUIDE

IF YOU ARE WALKING FOLKS
THROUGH THE MATERIAL OR
FACILITATING A GROUP, THE
LEADERS GUIDE IS FOR YOU!

The leaders guide can be found at the end of each section. We
encourage you to utilize it before each meeting. It is designed to
help you walk alongside someone on the journey, lead a couple
through the material, or facilitate a group. Our goal is to help you
lead in an effective and healthy way. You'll see the leaders guide
divided into 3 sections:

CONNECT WITH YOURSELF & GOD

The first section is specifically dedicated to self-intimacy.
Knowing ourselves is key to effective leadership and good
leaders go first. We need to be aware of what we are bringing to
the meeting that might inform how we lead; both what might
restrict our potential effectiveness and what may help us help
others. We also need to be plugged into the source of wisdom
and change. This is a chance to prayerfully connect with God
before connecting with other.

CONNECTWITH THE FOLKS YOU'RE HELPING

This section is meant to help you take what you know about the
people you're helping and merge the material with their story in
a meaningful way. We want you to craft questions that help them
move forward, as well as anticipate any challenges that might
arise from the material.

THE BIG PICTURE

Finally, this section is to give you a sense of what we had in
mind as the key takeaways for the section, and also what we
would be watching for if we were the leader/facilitator.

CONNECT WITH YOURSELF

6 FOUNDATIONS OF EFFECTIVE LEADING/FACILITATING

CAPACITY	**GROUNDING**
HUMILITY	**VULNERABILITY**
EMPATHY	**HOPE**

While there are a sundry of variables, traits and attributes that contribute to effective leadership, we've honed in on 6 that are foundational for walking with people on this particular journey. Over the next few pages you'll find definitions of these foundational attributes as well as descriptive scoring ranges. These are meant to give you a framework to assess yourself in these areas prior to each meeting. Using the descriptions, circle a number on the scale with 1 being lowest and 10 being highest to identify where you are at the moment. This is an opportunity to identify challenges to effectively leading as well as strengths to leverage for this meeting.

Each attribute has a low, medium and high range associated with it. The idea isn't to try and get all 10's; the idea is to honestly assess where you are at the moment. It's about awareness and self-intimacy. So if you score yourself in the low range on one of them, it simply means that 1) it could potentially hinder your leadership, and 2) there may be some steps you need to take to strengthen that area.

For example, maybe in your personal life you've had to revisit aspects of your own story that bring up old shame, and you find yourself wondering if it will ever truly be in the past. You might score a 1 on Capacity, because you are so engulfed in your own process, and a 2 in Hope because there is hopelessness about whether the shame will ever go away. Those things aren't bad or wrong per se; they just are. But if you enter into someone else's story with low capacity and hopelessness, you run the risk of them thinking they are a burden and believing they are hopeless and beyond any sort of redemption.

Having identified the 1 in Capacity and 2 in Hope, you may need to reach out to your

CONNECT WITH YOURSELF

6 FOUNDATIONS OF EFFECTIVE LEADING/FACILITATING

support community, spouse or trusted friend prior to the meeting. That way you can offload some of the burden, be encouraged about your own journey, and get some perspective to ratchet up the hope. You may not go from 1 to 10, but if you jump to a 5, and you are aware of your tendency for that number to drop given your current circumstance, you will be better prepared to walk the journey with the people you are helping.

We want you to be the most effective leader/facilitator you can be,; fully present, engaged and connected to the folks you are helping. We hope this self assessment helps toward that end.

The next few pages outline the definitions and descriptions. Each time you utilize the Leaders Guide at the end of a section, you can refer back here if needed to help complete the self-assessment portion.

#1 CONNECT WITH YOURSELF

6 FOUNDATIONS OF EFFECTIVE LEADING/FACILITATING

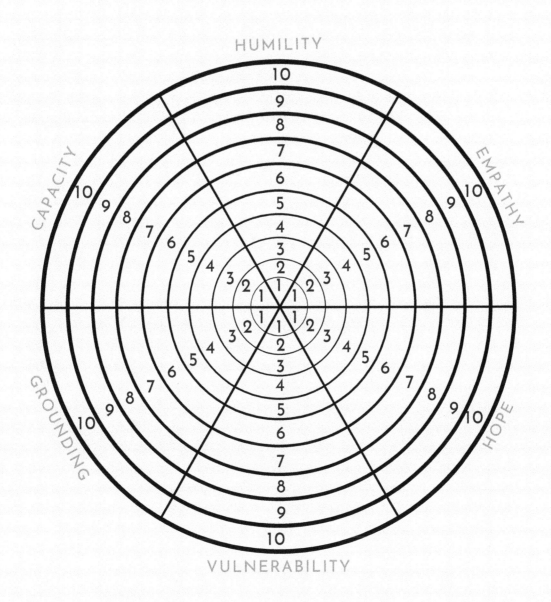

CONNECT WITH YOURSELF

CAPACITY

This is your capacity to hold other people's pain and sit with them in their struggle.

1 - 3 : low capacity = your plate is full, you are maxed out, you're dealing with a host of things in your own life that are taking up mental/emotional/spiritual/ bandwidth. The thought of helping shoulder someone else's burden sounds overwhelming right now.

4 - 7 : medium capacity = you have things going on, but they aren't weighing you down or using up all your bandwidth. You have margin to enter into someone else's pain, but only to a certain extent. You're open, but guarded about how much you can take on.

8 - 10 : high capacity = you have margin in this moment to fully enter into someone else's story, shoulder their burden with them, and not have to closely measure how much you are taking on. There is freedom to give yourself fully to the next meeting and the folks you are leading.

HUMILITY

Your connection to the gift of your own story and the grace you've experienced.

1 - 3 : low humility = Arrogance or ungratefulness is present and pervasive. Your sights are set inward instead of outward. Perhaps you are sitting on feelings of resentment, injustice or disappointment. Also could be haughtiness or pride of self accomplishment with regard to your own story.

4 - 7 : medium humility = pride/arrogance are on a teeter-totter with lowliness and sober assessment of yourself. At any moment you are thankful for your story, but that can quickly change to resentment or disappointment. Your sense of self accomplishment is also balanced against the sense of God's supernatural intervention in your life.

8 - 10 : high humility = you are in touch with your brokenness and depravity, yet grateful for your story. You're operating with a keen awareness that you are one bad decision away from destruction, yet gracefully living into the gift of freedom and redemption.

CONNECT WITH YOURSELF

EMPATHY

Your ability to meet someone in their emotion, feel it with them and feel for them.

1 - 3 : low empathy = your ability to get out of your own shoes and connect to someone's story is significantly diminished. To engage their experience in such a way that they feel felt seems nearly impossible. You may be self focused, wishing someone would feel your pain, even resenting you have to feel someone else's.

4 - 7 : medium empathy = you can feel someone else's pain and engage their experience but its a struggle between sympathy and empathy. There is a governor on your heart, preventing you from fully feeling the weght of their story.

8 - 10 : high empathy = you can set your story aside for this meeting, tenderly and compassionately connect to someone else's experience, and reflect back to them that you get it, you feel them, you're with them and you aren't going anywhere. You're engaged, willing to cry with them, grieve with them, and laugh with them .

GROUNDING

How centered you feel in light of what is happening in your own life. Knowing your true identity and living out of that.

1 - 3 : low grounding = perhaps you've been triggered back to shame or negative emotions within your own story or something else in your life. You are riding the roller coaster emotionally and can't quite get your feet under you. You aren't centered in your identity in Christ at this moment, but instead are drifting as you try to reconnect to who you really are.

4 - 7 : medium grounding = you alternate between centeredness, knowing your true identity and feeling confident in it, versus flailing, wondering if you are just an imposter. Your sense of self is at moments up for grabs, juggled back and forth between the truth and lies.

8 - 10 : high grounding = you are internalizing the truth of your identity and living out of that confident sense of self. You are emotionally stable, balanced and exhibiting sober judgement over how your emotions impact you. While you may not have all the answers, you feel ready to field what might come your way from the folks you are leading.

CONNECT WITH YOURSELF

VULNERABILITY

How open you feel to share your own story, both successes and struggles. Willingness to step forward when you have answers and also willing to admit when you don't.

1 - 3 : low vulnerability = you feel closed off, unwilling or uninterested in sharing your own journey. Whether highs or lows, success or failures, you aren't interested in self-disclosure at the moment, possibly fearing scrutiny or criticism.

4 - 7 : medium vulnerability = you measure how much self disclosure you're willing to engage. Perhaps willing to share highs but not lows, or unwilling to share when it might reflect poorly of you. Hesitant to lead from your own brokenness.

8 - 10 : high vulnerability = you're open to anything in your story being used to benefit someone else's story. You feel confident to share appropriately, not making it about yourself.

HOPE

Your sense of hope in redemption and restoration. Some days hope is alive and well, some days its hard to see how something so tangled and broken can be fixed.

1 - 3 : low hope = you are personally feeling a sense of hopelessness. Whether about your own story or the journey others are on, you are doubting if redemption is possible and maybe questioning if its worth the work.

4 - 7 : medium hope = you are waffling between hope and hopelessness. You know there's a light at the end of the tunnel, and you're pretty sure it's not an oncoming train. You are holding onto the truth of hope, even though you're having moments where it's hard to believe.

8 - 10 : high hope = you are living in hope, experiencing the reality that God is still in the business of Redemption. You have confidence in what God wants to redeem in someone else's story, even if you can't fathom how it would come to be.

CONNECT WITH YOURSELF

What did the latest content stir in you emotionally? How do you feel about engaging the people you are helping with this content?

Was there anything this week in your personal story that makes engaging this material easier or more challenging? What and why?

CONNECT WITH YOURSELF

Are you passing any judgements or holding any narratives about the folks you are helping that could adversely impact your leadership and/or their experience? If so why and how can you relinquish or resolve those judgements or narratives?

CONNECT WITH THE FOLKS YOU'RE HELPING

What can you see in the material that uniquely connects to the their story? What questions might be helpful to ask based on that?

Where can you anticipate the discussion might get challenging and how can you prepare for that?

BIG PICTURE

KEY POINTS FOR THIS SECTION

These are the key points we would want someone to walk away with if we were leading them through the material. We want to give you a starting point, but not an end point, as your intuition and the Holy Spirit will ultimately guide you.

WHAT TO WATCH FOR / BE AWARE OF

You'll see what to watch for in each section from what we typically see in husbands and wives going through the process.

FOR HUSBANDS

In this section we'll give you a heads-up on things we normally see come up for husbands that can delay or damage the trust-building process.

FOR WIVES

In this section we'll give you a heads-up on things we normally see come up for wives that can add unnecessary pain and confusion to the trust-building process.

01

INVESTING OUR RESOURCES

Trust is destroyed at her expense. Trust is rebuilt at his expense.

INVESTING OUR RESOURCES

INVESTING WHAT WE HAVE FOR THE SAKE OF WINNING BACK HER TRUST

 If you haven't already, please visit www.rebuildcourse.com to access the videos.

Rebuilding trust requires an investment. There's no way around it. As husbands, we've given time and energy to destruction, now we have to give time and energy to redemption. That includes our own personal journey of redemption and also weaving trust and security back into the fabric of the relationship. Our singular focus has to be redemption. It cannot compete with work, kids, school, family, money or hobbies. It can only come second to your faith journey.

For wives, the investment is risky. How much vulnerability, how much hope, how much willingness, grace, time, patience, trying to see the bright side or the best in her husband is a worthwhile investment to make? It is incredibly difficult to know in the face of very real hurt and the chance

that it happens all over again. One of the most spiritual and courageous things a wife who has been betrayed can do is simply wait. Patience is a virtue. Especially in the early days of discovery and disclosure. Sure there is pain to process and greiving to be done. That's work! But in terms of investing yourself in the healing process, our encouragement is to wait and watch.

Watch as he prioritizes recovery and redemption. Watch as he sheds the shame. Watch as he grows in faith and maturity. Wait while he fumbles and makes mistakes along the way (not continuing to act out, but the mistakes of relational immaturity). The fruit of all this work will be obvious. You'll be drawn to trust him.

INVESTING OUR RESOURCES

TIME

Recovery/Rebuilding trust has to be your top priority. This includes being a priority over your bowling league, your crossfit workouts and even your job. When it comes to providing security for your wife, how you invest your time is critical.

ENERGY

Energy – Digging into your past to uncover wounds, pain and the first signs of addiction can be very emotionally draining. You will need to dedicate energy to doing work as well as time for rest (NOTE: the amount of time you are resting should not be greater than the amount of time you are engaged in recovery work). Something or someone is going to get the best of you; i.e., the bulk of your energy. You get to decide who.

MONEY

Money - Financial investment into your future is money well spent. Think of all the resources you have poured into hobbies, dreams, and even your acting out in the past. While finances aren't the only factor, it is a factor, and one that can very tangibly point to recovery and rebuilding trust.

QUESTIONS FOR HIM

What hurdles do you see in the way of being committed to the healing process in terms of time, energy & resources?

How will you overcome the hurdles you have identified with regards to time, energy, and resources?

What is one thing you know will be a competing priority in your life and will have to be addressed?

QUESTIONS FOR HIM

Do you have a support system to help with accountability, community, and encouragement that is safe for you and your wife? If yes name those folks. If not, how will you develop that support system?

QUESTIONS FOR HER

What hurdles do you see in the way of being committed to the healing process in terms of time, energy & resources?

For some wives, waiting and watching feels powerless. For others it provides relief to be off the hook for carrying the relationship. Is it either of these for you? If so why? If not, how does waiting and watching feel to you?

QUESTIONS FOR HER

Do you have a support system to help with processing your story with safety and encouragement? If so, who are those people? If not, is it something you feel like you need right now? Is there anyone you could confide in to begin getting support?

WIVES SUPPORT GROUPS

Some wives find community through a professionally led support group offered by Redemptive Living for Women. You can find more information on those at www.rlforwomen.com.

COLOSSIANS 1:29

For this I toil, struggling with all his energy that he powerfully works within me.

PERSONAL REFLECTION

What does it mean for you to toil? And what does it mean that you toil with *his* (referring to God) energy?

LEADERS GUIDE

CONNECT WITH YOURSELF

6 FOUNDATIONS OF EFFECTIVE LEADING/FACILITATING

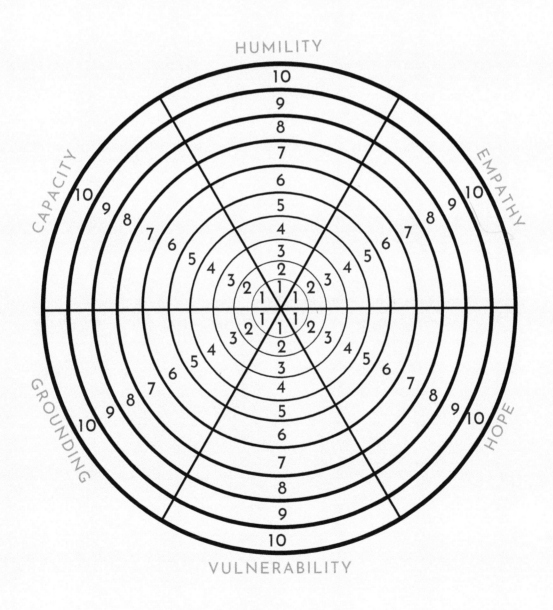

CONNECT WITH YOURSELF

What did the latest content stir in you emotionally? How do you feel about engaging the people you are helping with this content?

Was there anything this week in your personal story that makes engaging this material easier or more challenging? What and why?

CONNECT WITH YOURSELF

Are you passing any judgements or holding any narratives about the folks you are helping that could adversely impact your leadership and/or their experience? If so why and how can you relinquish or resolve those judgements or narratives?

CONNECT WITH THE FOLKS YOU'RE HELPING

What can you see in the material that uniquely connects to the their story? What questions might be helpful to ask based on that?

Where can you anticipate the discussion might get challenging and how can you prepare for that?

#3 BIG PICTURE

KEY POINTS FOR THIS SECTION

For men to restore trust, it will require sacrifice, commitment and investment.

Recovery, sanctification and relational restoration has to be top priority.

Wives need space to watch and wait.

WHAT TO WATCH FOR / BE AWARE OF

FOR HUSBANDS

■ Minimizing and dismissing her and the recovery process by:

1. Asking questions that show he is interested in the destination, not the journey. Ex. "How long does this process usually take? Two or three months?"

2. Resisting the disclosure process by making statements like, "How is it helpful for her to hear the details of my betrayal?"

3. Allowing the financial cost of the recovery work to be an issue by saying things like, "I'm not sure how long we can afford this."

FOR WIVES

■ Feeling pressure to make a definitive decision on the future.

1. Perhaps her husband is making statements like, "I'll do this if you will commit to staying in the marriage."

continued...

BIG PICTURE

WHAT TO WATCH FOR / BE AWARE OF

FOR WIVES

2. Pressure for or against divorce from her family (or his), pastor or friends.

▪ Patience is key right now, no decision has to be made about the future yet.

▪ Also, a support system for her is vital. She needs people to love and support her without judgment on her or him.

02

MYTHS 1 - 4

MYTHS 1 - 4

We've all been taught principles and philosophies, through family, friends and faith, that help us navigate life. Some become deeply meaningful and we find that we can lean on them for wise decisions. Others simply became mantras that give the appearance of being helpful and meaningful, but ultimately disappoint us.

The motivation for debunking these myths is to bypass some of the disappointment, but more importantly to set our beliefs and thinking on the right trajectory.

For wives, some of these myths appear to provide an explanation and give some semblance of understanding as to why these things have happened. They can hold hope and promise. But we don't want our hope in myths. We want our in the

Lord, and for the explanations to come from the work a husband does.

For husbands also, they myths can provide hope and something to lean on when things feel very powerless. But we want our agency to come from the Lord. Not from trite sayings. Further, there are myths we must address that handicap a man's progress in recovery because believing the myth will leave gaps in the work he must do. We, as husbands, can't allow the myths to be a window to look at our spouse, but rather a mirror to assess ourselves.

With a better understanding of the myths, and the associated truths, we'll be squarely set to do the work necessary for rebuilding trust.

MYTHS 1 - 4

 TIME HEALS ALL WOUNDS

 NOT ACTING OUT AGAIN IS ALL IT TAKES

 TRUST WILL BE RESTORED IF SHE STOPS BEING SO CONTROLLING

 HE WOULDN'T DO THIS IF HE REALLY LOVED ME

TIME HEALS ALL WOUNDS

MYTHS

TIME HEALS ALL WOUNDS

#1

The calendar does not fix trust. It's weird to think of it this way, isn't it? The essence of this myth is exactly that; marking days off the calendar will provide healing. But it doesn't work that way. Time certainly is an essential ingredient, but it doesn't remove the memory or the hurt.

Over time memories fade and details become fuzzy, seemingly disappearing from our consciousness. Until we are triggered. With little to no healing, any memory of the event becomes as fresh and tangible as the day it was experienced, and it's right back in the forefront of our minds.

However, when time is used in profound, intentional ways with compassion and empathy, the Holy Spirit interacts with our spirit and healing actually happens. Then, when triggers occur, the memories may return, but they won't feel so present. You'll know they are the past. They won't have the same pain with them. It will be something you remember, but no longer something that wrecks you.

QUESTIONS FOR BOTH

Is this myth one that you want to hold on to and believe in? if so, why? if not, why not?

Name emotional wounds in your life that time alone hasn't healed? What would you say has been missing that would've provided healing?

QUESTIONS FOR HIM

Is it daunting to think that time doesn't heal wounds and instead to think you are a co-conspirator with Christ in that process? Why or why not?

What fears do you have about making the most of each day for trustbuilding?

QUESTIONS FOR HER

What do you expect to see from your husband in terms of how he uses time in recovery and trustbuilding? What would you see that would make you feel hope?

Is there fear that he won't do the work, but instead will just hope that passing time will fix things? If so why, if not, why not?

MSG
EPHESIANS 5:16

Wake up from your sleep,
Climb out of your coffins;
Christ will show you the light!
So watch your step. Use your head. Make the most of every chance you get. These are desperate times!

PERSONAL REFLECTION

As a husband, how have you been asleep? Ahat have your coffins been? And what does it mean to you that these are desperate times?

As a wife, have you been asleep? And what does it mean in this season to watch your step?

NOT ACTING OUT AGAIN IS ALL IT TAKES

#2

MYTHS

Just because the habit gets healed doesn't mean the heart has.

NOT ACTING OUT AGAIN IS ALL IT TAKES

#2

If only it were this easy! If we just do what we were supposed to be doing (or not doing) then things would get patched right up. We wish! But it couldn't be farther from the truth. Continuing to act out in some way will absolutely delay your progress. It'll feel like you are constantly running with a parachute. Every episode of acting out will double-down on the shame, reset the clock on trust building and feel like 3 steps back for every step forward.

But, not acting out again doesn't necessarily guarantee an expedited process either! It means there is one less thing (albeit major) to slow y'all down. It means you as a man and husband can finally start to look at the real you. And don't forget the bigger picture; that acting out is just the expression of deeper character and sanctification issues.

Just because the habit gets healed doesn't mean the heart has. Sobriety gives us a solid footing for the real work of recovery and healing to happen.

QUESTION FOR BOTH

Is this myth one that you want to hold on to and believe in? if so, why? if not, why not?

QUESTIONS FOR HIM

Not acting out again is certainly something we want, but it is a low bar. What character traits are you striving to develop that will take you well beyond just not acting out?

Write 2 sentences to yourself to offset this myth. These are to serve as reminders of what the truth really is...that there's more to life and trustbuilding than just not acting out.

QUESTIONS FOR HIM

Sobriety, or no longer acting out, can sometimes feel like a huge accomplishment. We need men in our lives who can give us a high five for it. But we cannot expect it from our wives. Are you expecting her to celebrate your sobriety? if so why? if not, why not?

PS - if she is in a place to celebrate sobriety, consider it a huge gift!

QUESTIONS FOR HER

Do you fear him acting out again? Is there a part of you that wants to settle for the low bar of him just not acting out again? If so, why? If not, why not?

Take a moment to consider and write out why simple sobriety is not enough for redemption, and why you aren't willing to settle for less than him changing at his core.

HEBREWS 13:18

Pray for us. We are sure that we have a clear conscience and desire to live honorably in every way.

PERSONAL REFLECTION

As a husband, take a moment to prayerfully consider if you have a clear conscience. Is there anything else you need to tell your wife?

As a wife, what does it mean to you to live honorably in the middle of this painful process?

TRUST WILL BE RESTORED WHEN SHE STOPS
BEING SO CONTROLLING

#3

MYTHS

I'll make sure you're okay at my expense.

TRUST WILL BE RESTORED WHEN SHE STOPS BEING SO CONTROLLING

#3

Ouch! I (Jason) feel a twinge of pain even seeing this myth. Partly because of our personal story; I consistently criticized Shelley for being too controlling. It was manipulative and downright mean. I also feel pain seeing it because I've watched wife after wife in my office feel like they have lost themselves and become a shell of who they believed themselves to be. All because they were trying to avoid being the "nagging, controlling wife".

When a husband says or insinuates that his wife's control issues are the hold up to healing, he just adds insult to injury.

The real issue is not her control; it is his overcompensation. Pointing to her control is easier than acknowledging feeling powerless, hopeless or incompetent. Rather than honestly engage his insecurity, he'll call attention to hers.

What we hope husbands can start to see is that control isn't about her insecurity, it is about her lack of security.

This lack of security comes from the character issues we've exhibited that have hurt her and the relationship, as well as from the betrayal. Without realizing it, the message of your life has been, "I'll make sure I'm okay at your expense". That is a message of destruction.

Rebuilding trust requires a new message of redemption. One that says, "I'll make sure you're okay at my expense". It necessitates that a husband humbly take ownership for the damage he's

TRUST WILL BE RESTORED WHEN SHE STOPS BEING SO CONTROLLING

#3

caused and tenderly try to be a safe place for her to express pain. As a wife experiences her husband consistently protecting her instead of himself she'll feel more secure. And the more security she feels because of his actions, the less she has to control things through her own.

QUESTIONS FOR BOTH

Is this myth one that you want to hold on to and believe in? If so, why? If not, why not?

Take a moment and name one or two things that have been perceived as control, but instead can be seen as searching for security.

QUESTIONS FOR HIM

What does it get you to focus on her level of control? Perhaps a sense of being out of the spotlight or off the hot seat? Maybe it diminishes the shame or guilt because you're not "the only one with issues"?

In what ways can you see yourself sending the message "I'll make sure I'm okay at your expense"?

QUESTIONS FOR HIM

When we say "I'll make sure you're okay at my expense" we acknowledge it will cost us something. Try to name ways it will cost you according to the prompts below.

Example: Making sure she's okay when we're at church may cost me <u>friendships and being in choir/on the worship team.</u>

Making sure she's okay when we're out in public may cost me _____

_____

Making sure she's okay when we're at church may cost me _____

_____

It may cost me reputation when I choose to _____

_____

It may cost me embarassment when I choose to _____

_____

It may cost me freedom when I choose to _____

_____

It may cost me privacy when I choose to _____

_____

Any others you can think of?

QUESTIONS FOR HER

Have you been accused of being too controlling? If so, by whom and why? What were they focused on in the accusation?

We say that control is a search for security. What would you call it? What would you say you are needing when it has been mis-labeled as too controlling?

QUESTIONS FOR HER

In what ways can you identify that your husband has made sure he's okay at your expense? Can you recount specific instances?

Some wives say even when their husband is doing good work to help her feel secure, it's hard to let go of the reins. They say it can feel like easing up on control is giving him permission to hurt her all over again. Or that easing up is scary because he'll stop working as hard. What do you feel when you think about easing up and letting go of the reins?

JOB 11:18

You will be secure, because there is hope;
    you will look about you and take your rest in safety.

PERSONAL REFLECTION

As a husband, realize that providing security means providing hope.
How are you providing her hope?

As a wife, what does it mean to hope in your husband, as well as hope
in the Lord? Also, what does it mean to take your rest in safety?

HE WOULDN'T DO THIS IF HE REALLY LOVED ME

#4

MYTHS

HE WOULDN'T DO THIS IF HE REALLY LOVED ME

#4

"If he hurt me this bad he must not love me."
"He wouldn't do this to me if he really loved me."

"I must not love her; look at what I've done to her."
"I thought I loved her, but evidently I didn't."

These are statements wives and husbands make when trying to explain how love fits into this painful equation. It seems very binary; off or on, good or bad, love or hate. It can feel like the only explanation is hate. But there is a middle ground. There's a gray area where love isn't what it is supposed to be, but its also not void altogether.

For wives, this conversation can be infuriating. It can feel like an excuse, a rationalization and a minimization of her pain. Let me reassure you our aim is none of those.

We want to be able shed a little light on love. Maybe give words to something husbands have a difficult time articulating, while at the same time honoring that for a betrayed wife no answer is sufficient.

QUESTIONS FOR HIM

How have you reconciled loving her yet still doing these things, and how have you tried to communicate that to her?

If someone had no idea what love was, and had to define and describe it based on the way you've lived, how would they describe it?

QUESTIONS FOR HIM

Based on the last question, what do you feel? How do you think she would feel reading that description? What about it needs to change?

Describe how you can see your wife has tried to love you in the midst of how you've been living. Give specific examples.

QUESTIONS FOR HER

Can you reconcile that he did these things and simultaneously loved you? If so how? If not, why not?

Most wives look back, regardless of how long they've been married and regardless of whether or not she knew what was happening, and say "I tried to love you well". How have you tried to love him well?

QUESTIONS FOR HER

How do you feel about him saying, "I love you" today? Do you want to hear it? Is it empty? Infuriating? Reassuring? And how do you feel about reciprocating saying it?

MSG
PSALM 56:8

You've kept track of my every toss and turn
  through the sleepless nights,
Each tear entered in your ledger,
  each ache written in your book.

PERSONAL REFLECTION

Your grief isn't lost on God. You're seen; both of you. Every tear recorded, every toss and turn. How do you process knowing this truth? What do you feel?

PAUSE

We want to take a time out here. We've covered heavy stuff. Painful topics. This is no easy task. So, take a break and breathe. The next exercise is about grieving. It's simply a chance to process your experience at the moment. Then we'll get to the next section.

Remember that grieving is making sense of our story.

GRIEVING FOR WIVES

Remember that grieving is part of the process. You can think of grieving as 'making sense of my story'. Grieving is cyclical and iterative; it doesn't happen in one fell swoop. You have to cycle through it, revisiting some aspects of the betrayal multiple times (unfortunately). Four of the big stages of grief and examples of them are: Denial - I can't believe this is my life. Anger - I'm rightfully enraged about what has happened. Bargaining - negotiating with myself to try and stop the pain. And finally, Hopelessness - feeling despair and disbelief that things can change or be healed. All these stages are normal. Some last longer than others, and they can change on a dime (which is also normal).

Take a moment, identify and write down where you see these aspects of grief in your process right now.

DENIAL

Ex: "I can't believe he lied when we were engaged!"

ANGER

Ex: "I hate that he took away my voice, my say!"

GRIEVING FOR WIVES
CONTINUED

BARGAINING

Ex: "I'll stay til the kids leave, then I'm leaving."

HOPELESSNESS

Ex: "I can't imagine how I'll ever not worry about what he's doing on business trips."

As a wife, you're not crazy! You might be on the emotional crazy coaster, but you aren't crazy. You're grieving. When you feel your emotions change on a dime, love turn to hate, to a puddle on the floor, to just plain numb, remember that its normal. You'll get through this, and you'll get off the roller coaster. It won't last forever!

GRIEVING FOR HUSBANDS

Remember that grieving is part of the process. You can think of grieving as 'making sense of my story'. Grieving is cyclical and iterative; it doesn't happen in one fell swoop. You have to cycle through it, revisiting some aspects of the betrayal multiple times (unfortunately) as well as aspects of your acting out. Not in a way that relishes or romanticizes it, but in a way that sheds truth and light on just how dark it is.

Four of the big stages of grief along with examples are: Denial - I can't believe this is my life, I can't believe what I've done. Anger - I'm rightfully enraged about what I've done. Bargaining - negotiating with myself to try and stop the pain, to try to and figure out a way to salvage things. And finally, Hopelessness - feeling despair and disbelief that things can change or be healed. Just as for wives, these are all normal. They come in waves, and it won't last forever.

Take a moment, identify and write down where you see these aspects of grief in your process right now.

DENIAL

Ex: "I can't belive I got this far off the rails!"

ANGER

Ex: "I'm frustrated with myself and angry at myself for never being completely honest."

GRIEVING FOR HUSBANDS
CONTINUED

BARGAINING

Ex: "If I just left, she'd be better off."

HOPELESSNESS

Ex: "I can't imagine she'll ever love me again."

#2

LEADERS GUIDE

CONNECT WITH YOURSELF

6 FOUNDATIONS OF EFFECTIVE
LEADING/FACILITATING

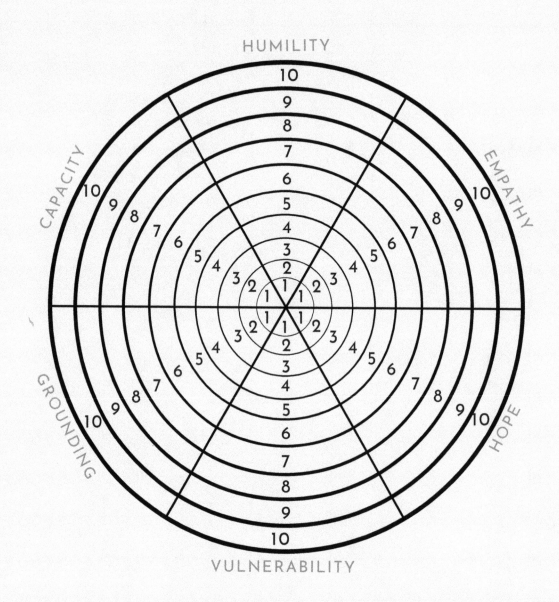

CONNECT WITH YOURSELF

What did the latest content stir in you emotionally? How do you feel about engaging the people you are helping with this content?

Was there anything this week in your personal story that makes engaging this material easier or more challenging? What and why?

CONNECT WITH YOURSELF

Are you passing any judgements or holding any narratives about the folks you are helping that could adversely impact your leadership and/or their experience? If so why and how can you relinquish or resolve those judgements or narratives?

CONNECT WITH THE FOLKS YOU'RE HELPING

What can you see in the material that uniquely connects to the their story? What questions might be helpful to ask based on that?

Where can you anticipate the discussion might get challenging and how can you prepare for that?

BIG PICTURE

KEY POINTS FOR THIS SECTION

The myths create/perpetuate faulty beliefs that negatively impact the process. We want to start on solid ground and give folks a clear picture of what they are engaging.

This section is continuing to shift the weight of responsibility on to a husband's shoulders and give a wife relief from having to do the work.

WHAT TO WATCH FOR / BE AWARE OF

FOR HUSBANDS

■ Resistance to see a heart change and focusing on a behavioral change in recovery by him making statements like "well I'm not acting out anymore" or "I've had sobriety for ____ days, months, years."

■ "IF SHE" syndrome. His potential to blame shift by making hurtful statements like, "if she would get over this we could move on" or "if she would stop controlling my every move, I could show her I won't act out anymore."

■ His feelings of powerlessness coming out as resignation and defeat using statements like, "I'll never be different in her eyes" or "I guess I'll just trade in the smart phone for a dumb phone" said with a condescending tone.

continued...

#3 BIG PICTURE

WHAT TO WATCH FOR / BE AWARE OF

FOR WIVES

- Her taking responsibility for his work or his acting out.
    1. Saying things like, "I haven't been very attentive to his sexual needs lately" or the opposite "I have given him sex whenever he wanted it, even when I didn't want to."

- Making statements about feeling like she has to be his mom to get him to treat her well.

- Ultimately she needs space to work through and process the myths and how they might play out in her story. Don't be afraid to ask specific questions regarding their story to help her process.

03

MYTHS 5 - 8

MYTHS 5 - 8

A DEBUNKING PROJECT

In this section we are continuing to debunk the myths. At this point, you have a good sense for what that looks like. We have to challenge the myths to get to the truth. Whether you still find yourself wanting to believe them, or wishing you didn't believe them, they just require a sober scrutiny.

For wives, as you continue to work through these, take note of where a nerve really gets hit. When the pain is acute, it tells us there is history that will need to be dealt with. There will be new grieving to find healing.

For husbands, continue to challenge yourself to be on the hook for the work. As we've discussed, the myths can sometimes feel like a pass on persistence. Pay close attention to anything in the myths that prompts you to think "there's nothing I can

do about that" or "we'll just have to wait and see". Those may in fact be the areas with the most opportunity for you to make a difference.

Myths 5-8 are difficult but we need to address them. Let's go.

MYTHS 5 - 8

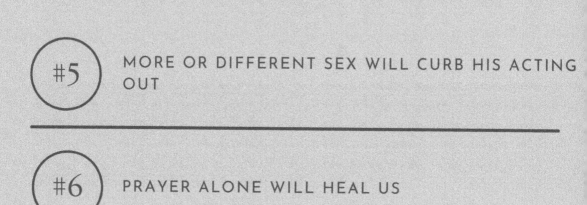

#5   MORE OR DIFFERENT SEX WILL CURB HIS ACTING OUT

#6   PRAYER ALONE WILL HEAL US

#7   TRUST WILL BE RESTORED WHEN SHE FORGIVES

#8   GOD WILL MIRACULOUSLY DELIVER ME FROM BEING TEMPTED AND OUR MARRIAGE FROM THIS PAIN

MORE OR DIFFERENT SEX WILL CURB HIS ACTING
OUT

#5

MYTHS

MORE OR DIFFERENT SEX WILL CURB HIS ACTING OUT

#5

This one seems to make sense on the surface. And it appears to be biblically backed! But things aren't always what they seem. This myth, along with misapplied theology, unfortunately creates a dynamic that degrades a wife's dignity. It can relegate her to an object that mechanically provides "relief" for her husband. That's terrible.

Insidiously, this myth also perpetuates a message that if a wife doesn't want to be cheated on then she better make herself available sexually. As if a sexless marriage means a spouse is destined for infidelity?

Dismantling this myth means restoring dignity to wives, as well as agency to husbands. We are not neanderthals driven by primal desires and therefore destined to cheat if she won't engage sexually. In fact, what if we're actually empowered to be agents of change and healing in the sexually intimate parts of our relationship?

That doesn't happen by changing the way we do sex; it changes by becoming deeply intimate.

QUESTIONS FOR BOTH

Is this myth one that you want to hold on to and believe in? If so, why? If not, why not?

How has your faith journey informed this myth? Have you heard this taught at church? What do you think about it today?

QUESTIONS FOR HIM

Is it difficult to let go of the idea that her level of willingness sexually is a deterrent to your acting out? If so, why? If not, why not?

For some of us, sexuality gets so much focus because it is the primary way to feel love and acceptance. For others, it gets attention because its missing altogether. Which is it for you and why?

QUESTIONS FOR HIM

How would you describe what sexual intimacy should be in a marriage? What should drive it, what should it mean, why should it even happen? And when should it not happen?

QUESTIONS FOR HER

Is it difficult to let go of the idea that your level of willingness sexually is a deterrent to his acting out? If so, why? If not, why not?

Some wives say they want the sexual intimacy after betrayal to increase. Others say they can't even imagine engaging sexually. Where are you with sexual intimacy right now and why?

QUESTIONS FOR HER

Do you feel pressure to engage sexually at this point? If yes, why? What voices do you hear putting pressure on you (pastor, husband, friend, mom, your own)? If not, what makes you feel safe and that the pressure is off?

Many wives have had this myth used as leverage and manipulation against them. Do you feel like its been used against you? If so, why? If not, why not?

QUESTIONS FOR HER

Especially if you've felt manipulated with regard to sexual intimacy, there may be some new boundaries you need to feel safe. Can you identify boundaries you know you need at this point as it pertains to sexual intimacy?

Is there anything about setting boundaries relative to sexual intimacy that feels like it contradicts the "do not withhold" scriptures you've been taught?

MATTHEW 22:15

Then the Pharisees went out and laid plans to trap him in his words.

PERSONAL REFLECTION

if you read the context for this verse, The pharisees tried to manipulate jesus by using scripture. some of us have either used scripture to manipulate, or had scripture used to manipulate us. how do you relate to what jesus experienced here?

MSG

JUDE 1:10

But these people sneer at anything they can't understand, and by doing whatever they feel like doing—living by animal instinct only—they participate in their own destruction.

PERSONAL REFLECTION

as we said in the opening of this section, we are not neanderthals, driven by some primal desire. when we live that way, we participate in our own destruction. how can you see this prove true in your life?

There are two Scripture Focus pages in this section intentionally.

♯6

MYTHS

PRAYER ALONE WILL HEAL US

#6

Let's first say, for the record, that diligent and pleading prayer in this process is absolutely essential. In fact, from a faith perspective, I see secular couples find restoration from sexual betrayal, but I see couples who put God at the center of their process genuinely experience Redemption. They don't just survive, they thrive. And prayer is a critical component.

But that can't be all there is. God is a god of action. His people are people of action. Sometimes we confuse the process and the outcome. God is responsible for the outcome and we are responsible for executing the process. If, as husbands, all we do is pray for a different life but never take a step in a new direction, we'll end up disappointed. We all know this experientially, whether in finances, weight loss, work, parenting; you name it. We don't pray for money and not work. We don't pray for great, mature kids, but sit on the couch and refuse to parent. We don't pray for weight loss while we down donuts (ok, guilty on this one). Anyway, you get the point.

Sometimes prayer can be an excuse for inaction. We can use it to remove ourselves from responsibility. But we have to balance and hold the tension between prayerful reliance on God and diligent effort on our part.

Let's pray like it all depends on God and work like it all depends on us.

QUESTIONS FOR HIM

Have you been confusing the outcome with the process? What do you think and feel when you consider that the process is up to you and the outcome is up to God?

What has your faith journey taught you about the power of prayer? And how does it line up with or contradict this myth?

QUESTIONS FOR HIM

When you think of redemption and thriving, not just restoration and surviving, what does it mean to you? How would you describe the difference, and how can you imagine it in your relationship?

Name a time or two when you've used prayer as an excuse for inaction. Also, can you see where you might be tempted to do that in this process? If so, how? If not, why not?

QUESTIONS FOR HER

What do you think and feel when you consider that the process is up to your husband and the outcome is up to God?

What has your faith journey taught you about the power of prayer? How does it line up with or contradict this myth?

QUESTIONS FOR HER

Have you experienced your husband using prayer as an excuse to not do the hard work? If yes, how does it make you feel when he does that? If no, how does it make you feel that he doesn't do that?

Are there any voices in your world right now that seem to be communicating you are expecting too much of your husband and not enough of God? If so what does it make you think and feel?

PROVERBS 21:31

The laborers who carried the loads worked with one hand and held a weapon with the other.

PERSONAL REFLECTION

Nehemiah tells us that the folks rebuilding the wall of Jerusalem was a good work, with enemies who wanted that good work to end. Such is the case for us. Prayer alone will not complete the good work of trust building. In fact, we'll likely need to fight for it while we build it.

Husbands, what does it look like to have a tool in one hand and a weapon in the other?

Wives, what enemies are trying to slow down your good work?.

TRUST WILL BE RESTORED WHEN SHE FORGIVES ME

#7

MYTHS

TRUST WILL BE RESTORED WHEN SHE FORGIVES ME

#7

This one may be the most overused myth of them all. And it's the one that seems to have the most truth in it. It's just not the whole truth. We all know (especially wives) that forgiveness is an integral part of the process. We all know biblically the call to forgive is expressly defined. But what is so often missed is that forgiveness in itself does not restore trust. In fact, forgiveness in this context changes more for the forgiver than for the forgiven. There is usually also a heavy expectation for forgiveness to be immediate.

Both husbands and wives often believe when forgiveness happens there will be no more questions, no more pain and no more anger.

Our God isn't a god with a bad memory. Jesus' work on the cross didn't erase the hard drive of God's mind. We have to remember that even God himself isn't a God of forgive and forget. If he were, we wouldn't have the Bible, as it is partly a record of wrongs (of course we also know its a record of redemption too). God is omniscient, thus he cannot forget. He's a God of forgive and never, ever hold it against us, because of the work of Jesus on the cross.

The Scriptures tell us that God will "remember our sins no more", and that he'll remove them "as far as the east is from the west". The essence of both of these is less about the mind of God and more about the heart of God. Specifically, His heart of Grace. I wonder if sometimes we want God to forgive and forget because we want to forgive and forget ourselves. But here's the thing; if that's really all there is to it, perhaps it shortchanges His grace.

TRUST WILL BE RESTORED WHEN SHE FORGIVES ME

#7

Might it help us see God in greater glory if we are aware that He knows every single sin we've ever committed yet chooses to never, ever hold it against us? That's amazing! Maybe instead of hoping to forget what we've done, we can start leveraging the memory of our sin to look at the magnitude of His grace. When we see it this way, it can help us be more humble and cultivate gratitude.

Taking it a step further, let's apply the same principle to our wives. Her forgiveness is less about her memory and more about her heart. It doesn't mean she'll never bring things up, it means she'll try her best and lean on God to not hold it against us. That is an immense act of grace. Recognizing her grace can lead us to humility and gratitude.

One other note on forgiveness....

Quite often fast forgiveness leads to delayed bitterness. Please, for both of your sakes, do not rush forgiveness. For many wives forgiveness genuinely comes on the other side of grief. Allow yourself space for grieving. Husbands, remember that her grieving is healing. We can't rush that process. When the focus is on her forgiveness it can feel like it is making her the problem, rather than the pain we've caused. The net effect of that will be increased bitterness.

Patience in this facet of the process is critical. Trust that God is at work. He wants y'alls healing more than anyone else in the world!

QUESTIONS FOR HIM

Describe your understanding of forgiveness; does it mean no more anger, no more bringing it up, no more pain? Where did you get these ideas?

Forgiveness means she's letting you off the hook from repaying a debt you cannot pay. Once the debt is cancelled, many wives fear their husband will go back to old ways. How can you reassure her that's not the case for you?

QUESTIONS FOR HIM

Do you want to forget your sins? That desire can change when we move from remembering the pain of our sin to dwelling on the grace of God. How can you dwell on God's grace in this season?

Even if you don't buy this grace stuff, can you agree that pressuring her to forgive will only serve to develop resentment and bitterness? If so, why? If not, why not?

QUESTIONS FOR HER

Do you feel pressure to forgive your husband? Why? From where or whom is that pressure coming?

Do you believe that forgiveness will mean you forget? That you'll never feel compelled to bring up the past? That you'll not be angry? If so, why? If not, why not?

QUESTIONS FOR HER

If you, your husband, your pastor....who ever you feel pressure from were to take the pressure off, how would it change your process right now?

Remember that grief can be confused with un-forgiveness. They are not the same. How would you describe the difference? And what might you need from your husband in light of this?

QUESTIONS FOR HER

How can your support system help you in your grieving and forgiveness process?

ISAIAH 53:3
DEUTERONOMY 31:8

[Jesus] - a man of suffering, and familiar with pain.

"The Lord, himself, goes before you and will be there with you. He will never leave you nor forsake you. Do not be afraid; do not be discouraged."

PERSONAL REFLECTION

Jesus was familiar with pain. He was connected with suffering and he is committed to walking with you. What does walking with him today mean when it comes to forgiveness?

Husbands, what does it mean to walk with him while working to forgive yourself?

GOD WILL MIRACULOUSLY DELIVER ME FROM
BEING TEMPTED AND OUR MARRIAGE FROM THIS
PAIN

♯8

MYTHS

Around provides relief, but through develops character and faith.

GOD WILL MIRACULOUSLY DELIVER ME FROM BEING TEMPTED AND OUR MARRIAGE FROM THIS PAIN

#8

Deliverance is so appealing. Jesus even prayed for it. But God typically goes through rather than around. Around provides relief, but through develops character and faith. Through means depending on His strength, leaning in to obedience, surrendering our will, and becoming the conduit of healing in our relationships.

Some faith backgrounds do truly believe in miraculous delivery from temptation and instantaneous healing from pain. I believe both of those can happen. I just don't see it happen often. Just like the prayer alone myth, we have to operate as active agents in the process while we are awaiting our deliverance. The Israelites had to enter the promised land; the land under their feet didn't just become the promised land. Jesus went to the cross; it didn't come to him.

Think of it this way: let's seek deliverance, while praying for deliverance, as we try to be an agent of deliverance.

QUESTIONS FOR HIM

For some men, the lack of deliverance brings up resentment toward God. They are hurt that God even let them behave this way in the first place. Is there resentment or hurt for you with God? If so, why? If not, why not?

How do you feel about the idea that together, you and God can redeem what has been broken? How would you describe your role in that partnership?

QUESTIONS FOR HIM

Consider for a moment that God is taking you through this rather than around it to grow your character. What character traits/fruits of the Spirit can you identify that may be getting worked on and cultivated?

How would the traits you identified above contribute to sexual integrity and marital redemption?

QUESTIONS FOR HER

When all you want is deliverance, for the pain to stop, what can you lean on to remember this isn't permanent? Are there scriptures, sayings, quotes, pictures, etc. that remind you of hope?

For some wives, well meaning people suggesting that healing will be found in deliverance creates the sense that she's the problem. As if somehow deliverance would be happening if she wasn't slowing things down. Do you ever feel this way? If so why? If not, why not?

QUESTIONS FOR HER

How does it make you feel to think that your husband may be the conduit God uses for your healing? Is that even remotely in the realm of possibility if he's the one who hurt you?

PSALM 34:18

The Lord is close to the brokenhearted
  and saves those who are crushed in spirit.

PERSONAL REFLECTION

How do you experience the truth that while there may not be miraculous deliverance, there will always be the promise of God's presence?

PAUSE

We want to take a time out here. We've covered heavy stuff. Painful topics. This is no easy task. So, take a break and breathe. The next exercise is about grieving. It's simply a chance to process your experience at the moment. Then we'll get to the next section.

Remember that grieving is making sense of our story.

GRIEVING FOR WIVES

Remember that grieving is part of the process. You can think of grieving as 'making sense of my story'. Grieving is cyclical and iterative; it doesn't happen in one fell swoop. You have to cycle through it, revisiting some aspects of the betrayal multiple times (unfortunately). Four of the big stages of grief and examples of them are: Denial - I can't believe this is my life. Anger - I'm rightfully enraged about what has happened. Bargaining - negotiating with myself to try and stop the pain. And finally, Hopelessness - feeling despair and disbelief that things can change or be healed. All these stages are normal. Some last longer than others, and they can change on a dime (which is also normal).

Take a moment, identify and write down where you see these aspects of grief in your process right now.

DENIAL

Ex: "I can't believe I didn't trust my intuition. "

ANGER

Ex: "I 'm angry that I gave him my body and he put my physical health in jeopardy. "

GRIEVING FOR WIVES
CONTINUED

BARGAINING

Ex: "God I'll never ___ if you will _____."

HOPELESSNESS

Ex: "He'll never change. He's been this way for too long."

As a wife, you're not crazy! You might be on the emotional crazy coaster, but you aren't crazy. You're grieving. When you feel your emotions change on a dime, love turn to hate, to a puddle on the floor, to just plain numb, remember that its normal. You'll get through this, and you'll get off the roller coaster. It won't last forever!

GRIEVING FOR HUSBANDS

Remember that grieving is part of the process. You can think of grieving as 'making sense of my story'. Grieving is cyclical and iterative; it doesn't happen in one fell swoop. You have to cycle through it, revisiting some aspects of the betrayal multiple times (unfortunately) as well as aspects of your acting out. Not in a way that relishes or romanticizes it, but in a way that sheds truth and light on just how dark it is.

Four of the big stages of grief along with examples are: Denial - I can't believe this is my life, I can't believe what I've done. Anger - I'm rightfully enraged about what I've done. Bargaining - negotiating with myself to try and stop the pain, to try to and figure out a way to salvage things. And finally, Hopelessness - feeling despair and disbelief that things can change or be healed. Just as for wives, these are all normal. They come in waves, and it won't last forever.

Take a moment, identify and write down where you see these aspects of grief in your process right now.

DENIAL

Ex: "This wouldn't have happened if our culture wasn't so sexualized."

ANGER

Ex: "I'm mad at the church for not teaching about this enough.".

GRIEVING FOR HUSBANDS
CONTINUED

BARGAINING

Ex: "I'll do the work as long as she commits to stay."

HOPELESSNESS

Ex: "There's too much water under the bridge for us to survive this."

#3

LEADERS GUIDE

CONNECT WITH YOURSELF

6 FOUNDATIONS OF EFFECTIVE
LEADING/FACILITATING

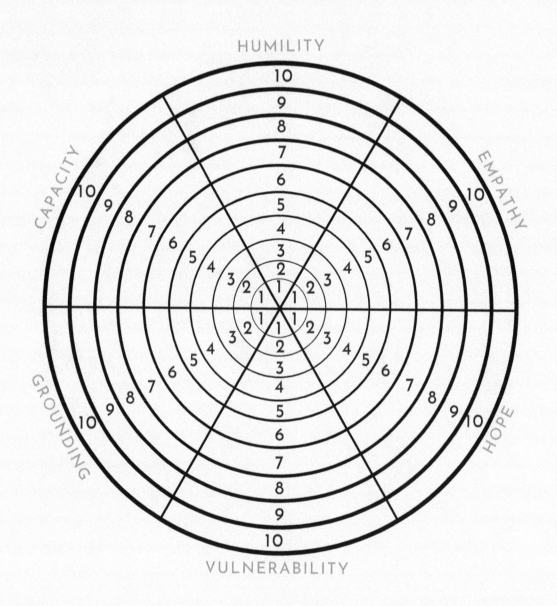

CONNECT WITH YOURSELF

What did the latest content stir in you emotionally? How do you feel about engaging the people you are helping with this content?

Was there anything this week in your personal story that makes engaging this material easier or more challenging? What and why?

CONNECT WITH YOURSELF

Are you passing any judgements or holding any narratives about the folks you are helping that could adversely impact your leadership and/or their experience? If so why and how can you relinquish or resolve those judgements or narratives?

#2 CONNECT WITH THE FOLKS YOU'RE HELPING

What can you see in the material that uniquely connects to the their story? What questions might be helpful to ask based on that?

Where can you anticipate the discussion might get challenging and how can you prepare for that?

#3 BIG PICTURE

KEY POINTS FOR THIS SECTION

Holding the tension of different faith journeys with different belief systems around deliverance and the miraculous against the reality of our intentionality and effort.

Moving sexual intimacy out of focus; giving husbands a higher horizo and wives a pass on the pressure.

We also want to be fostering the dialogue between a couple and mindful as leaders that we aren't just playing referee.

WHAT TO WATCH FOR / BE AWARE OF

FOR HUSBANDS

▪ Resistance to humility and ownership.
1. His inability or unwillingness to see and accept that his acting out sexually isn't about what kind or how often sex is happening in his marriage.

2. Praying his way out of a behavioral situations and expecting a miraculous change in the marriage. This requires little to no trust rebuilding work done on his part.

3. His unspoken (or spoken in some cases) expectations and conditions around forgiveness. Example: "If I do these couple things she will forgive me and we can get back to normal."

#3 **BIG PICTURE**

WHAT TO WATCH FOR / BE AWARE OF

FOR WIVES

- Feeling pressure to be working on "her part".
    1. Reassuring wives that they don't have to do work right now. It's ok to wait and see if he will do the trust building work. This will not break the process.

- Feeling pressure for quick forgiveness that doesn't require a process.
    1. Encouraging the wives to grieve and not put a time frame on it.

- Reassure her that she is worth raising the bar for him relationally and any resistance to that isn't a reflection of her worth; rather it is anindicator of his relational work ethic.

04

NON-NEGOTIABLES
PART 1

NON-NEGOTIABLES PART 1

THE BASICS THAT MUST BE IN PLACE FOR TRUST TO BE RESTORED

The non-negotiables are those basic, fundamental pieces that have to be in place for everything or anything else to be built. In sports or artistry, there are non-negotiables; feet placement, blocking and tackling, brushstrokes, color complementing. Parts of the overall whole that need to be revisited repeatedly, to be sure that the base is solid. Anything built on the foundation will eventually crumble if the base is shaky. So it is with trust building.

These fundamental elements ensure that the work we do, day-in-and-day-out, have a solid place to stand. When any of them are flimsy or begin to weaken, the whole structure starts to get wonky. The Lego sculpture starts to wobble. Experientially, wives can feel and sense the wobble. Their

fear increases, trust diminishes and the benefit of the doubt starts to wane. We cannot afford that if we're going to find redemption!

As you engage each of these, remember that not every one can be accomplished in entirety, immediately. Spiritual commitment is a journey, developing intimacy is a process and cultivating deeper accountability relationships takes time. Some are immediate though; like radical honesty and transparency.

Remember heart matters here. Your motivation and sincerity will show through by how you prioritize these in your life, how diligently you pursue them, and by how connected you are to her experience throughout.

NON-NEGOTIABLES PART 1

SPIRITUAL COMMITMENT

Betrayal impacts our spiritual journey. For some people, husbands and wives alike, there is a nearness wih God unlike ever before. For others there is a distance like never before. It challenges our theology, sometimes further solidifying it and sometimes making it feel even more confusing. Either way, it requires leaning in. Engaging is active not passive.

For folks from a Bible-based faith background, this is usually a key element in trust building. Wives want to see their husband sincerely engaging God; even if it's messy and convoluted. Now, there are times when a wife will say she can't handle floundering in faith. Understandably that just adds to the insecurity of an already upside down situation. But even if that's the case, she needs to know there is engagement.

As a husband, remember that working out your faith runs concurrently with working recovery and marital restoration. Our perspective is that they all work together, in an interwoven way.

At the end of this section there are a couple of books that can help as you navigate your faith journey.

QUESTIONS FOR HIM

Take a moment to describe your faith journey. Specifically speak to where you've been and where you are today as you work through this material.

QUESTIONS FOR HIM

What disciplines do you need to start or ramp-up in order to further develop your relationship with God?

What in your life might need to be removed or replaced to connect your heart with God's and your spirit with the Holy Spirit? (examples: replace tv with devotional time, removing hobbies that perpetuate checking out, turning off the radio and listening to a podcast sermon on your commute, removing noise and practicing silence)

QUESTIONS FOR HIM

Describe the impact of recovery on your faith journey. Has it distanced you from God? Brought you closer? Made you skeptical? Changed your idea of who He is?

QUESTIONS FOR HER

Describe how you view your husband's faith journey to this point and now in this course. Does it leave you encouraged or discouraged? Hopeful or hopeless?

Is seeing his spiritual commitment important to you? If not, why not? If so, what do you feel when you see him pursuing God and his faith?

QUESTIONS FOR HER

Describe the impact of betrayal on your faith journey. Has it distanced you from God? Brought you closer? Made you skeptical? Changed your view of Him?

What is the most comforting or reassuring element of his faith journey? Some wives say its him praying for them, or seeing him in the word, or him initiating going to church.

DEUTERONOMY 4:29

But if from there you seek the Lord your God, you will find him if you seek him with all your heart and with all your soul.

PERSONAL REFLECTION

What does it mean to you to seek God with all your heart and soul? And what does it mean to "find him" in this trust-building process?

BOOKS

With - Skye Jethani

Abba's Child - Brennan Manning

Anatomy of the Soul - Curt
Thompson

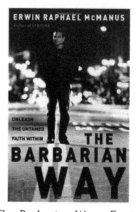

The Barbarian Way - Erwin
McManus

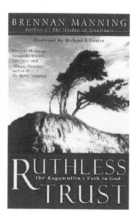

Ruthless Trust - Brennan Manning

God Stories - Andrew Wilson

NON-
NEGOTIABLES
PART 1

RADICAL HONESTY & TRANSPARENCY

Radical honesty and transparency are so important for a host of reasons, but one of the primary is that they both mitigate FEAR. Fear is the base level emotional driver on wives' lack of trust. Just to put a voice to it and name a few of the fears:

Fear of being duped again, made to feel like a fool.
Fear of being abandoned and rejected.
Fear of a final stamp of inadequacy.
Fear of being crazy.
Fear of being perpetually depressed or angry.
Fear of losing themselves.
Fear of physical harm.
Fear of today.
Fear of the future.
Fear of the impact on the kids.
Fear that she'll never be okay.

While we cannot answer every question and provide ultimate security against all her fears, we can be a co-conspirator with Christ in providing the safest space she's ever experienced. We can give her ammunition to fight the battles in her head. We can give her a parachute when it feels like she's in a free fall.

And one way we do that is by dealing in 100% truth. Nothing vague, nothing shaded, no more manipulation, no more crazy gymnastics to manange her thoughts and emotions.

Just the truth.

QUESTIONS FOR HIM

Are you willing to tell her the absolute truth even if it means she'll leave? If so, why? If not, why not?

Name your fears of telling the truth. What are you afraid of for her, for you and for others? Also, describe what it has cost you to sit on secrets.

QUESTIONS FOR HIM

In what areas of your life do you need an upgrade in terms of radical honesty? In what areas will it be most difficult?

Describe the difference between active and passive truth-telling. Also describe how you can see active truth-telling being helpful to your wife. In what areas of your life does this shift need to occur?

QUESTIONS FOR HIM

Why do you sometimes operate in a translucent way, where the truth isn't exactly clear? What does it get you? How does it protect you emotionally?

In what areas of your life do you need to practice full transparency? Where are you sufficiently vague and why? Remember this applies across the whole of our lives, not just in our marriages.

Think about when you've been lied to. What did you feel and why? How did it make you feel towards that person?

QUESTIONS FOR HIM

Sometimes it is not a matter of hiding, its a matter of detail and simply not knowing that she needs something more or different. If you haven't already discussed it, ask your wife what areas of your life she needs more transparency in. Describe your response to her requests.

A NOTE ABOUT TRANSPARENCY
One of the worst violations for wives is the violation of their intuition. It becomes difficult for some wives to trust their gut. It can cause them to second guess what they believe the Holy Spirit is telling them. And it creates tremendous anxiety. For more on this check out the podcast episode titled, "Anxiety, Women's Intuition and Trust".
https://www.rlforwomen.com/podcast/8-anxiety-womens-intuition-and-trust

QUESTIONS FOR HER

In what areas or on what issues do you feel like you aren't getting the absolute truth or transparency at the level you need?

In what areas do you need to see him actively truth telling, overcomunicating about what is happening (obviously, all!)?

QUESTIONS FOR HER

Describe what you feel when there isn't 100% transparency. What does it make you question about yourself? About him?

What, if any, areas of your life do you feel conviction to be radically honest with him about?

A NOTE ABOUT SAFETY

Some wives do not feel safe enough at this point to talk about areas of their life where radical honesty is needed. If that is true for you, please confide in one of the women you trust who are supporting you. While now may not be the time to talk with your husband about it, you also shouldn't sit with any secrets.

LUKE 12:2

There is nothing concealed that will not be disclosed, or hidden that will not be made known.

PERSONAL REFLECTION

No more secrets. No more lies. No more hiding. Everything made known. That day is coming, ultimately, but we have a chance to expedite it and make someday today. What do you feel and think when you reflect on this?

NON-NEGOTIABLES PART 1

We'll never fully accept acceptance until we're fully known.

TRUE INTIMACY

True intimacy; being fully known and fully knowing. By the very nature of it, you can see that true intimacy is impossible with lies and secrets. You're becoming well aware of what breaks down intimacy, but what builds it up? That's where these 3 distinct areas come into focus: Spiritual Intimacy, Emotional Intimacy and Intellectual Intimacy. Spirit, heart and mind are our starting point. For too many of us, our starting point is our body. In this context, post-betrayal, we want to move away from that. We don't want to discard it, but we want to put it in its rightful place.

Learning to be intimate in non-touch and non-sexual ways gives us a chance to experience a new and different depth of connection.

Also important to realize for some people the absence of conflict feels like intimacy. As long as we're getting along, then we must be connected. But that's not necessarily true, and as we are learning to connect in these core ways we will begin to experience the difference. We'll see that not only is conflict intimacy too, but the intimacy in the absence of conflict will be sweeter and more rewarding.

There are a couple of caveats with this section that are important for us to address. First, this has to be taken at a wife's pace. For some wives, too much intimacy too fast in the aftermath of betrayal is overwhelming and actually pushes them away. If you, as a wife, need to pace yourself

TRUE INTIMACY

(and him) with how much of these 3 intimacies you're engaging, please use your voice and communicate that. The last thing we want is for you to feel pressure, like you have to engage this way, and if you don't somehow you are slowing down the process. That's just not true. You get veto power, and get to decide the pace.

Second, for some couples this section is kind of backwards from what they've experienced. There has been spiritual, emotional and intellectual intimacy but the major gap has been in physical and sexual intimacy. It's not uncommon, and we talk to couples regularly where the husband has a ton of fear and anxiety around engaging sexually with his wife. Some couples haven't been sexually intimate in decades. It can be embarrassing and confusing for men, but also embarrassing and downright painful and rejecting for wives (even more true if he's been acting out sexually with pornography or another person). This is all rooted in Intimacy Aversion - the reluctance to engage in deep connected intimacy. If this is part of your story please take it delicately and with discernment.

A NOTE ABOUT INTIMACY AVERSION

Intimacy Aversion informs the way we connect with ourselves, with God, with our wives and with other people generally. If intimacy scares you or seems like a concept you need more help with, please consider taking our Intimacy Aversion Masterclass. www.redemptiveliving.com/intimacy-aversion

FOUNDATIONS OF INTIMACY

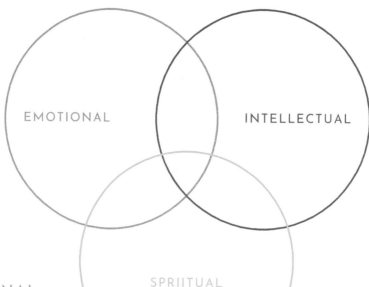

EMOTIONAL

INTELLECTUAL

SPRIITUAL

EMOTIONAL
Connection to your heart and your emotions. Your ability to communicate what you feel and why. Also, your connection to someone else's heart and emotions through empathy.

SPIRITUAL
How you connect around faith and your faith journey. This includes things like scripture, prayer, gifting, theology and worship.

INTELLECTUAL
This is connection around what you are thinking, why , and how you are thinking about things. It includes your hopes, dreams, passions, etc.

QUESTIONS FOR HIM

HOW WELL DO YOU CONNECT TO YOUR OWN EMOTIONS?

CIRCLE A NUMBER FOR YOUR ANSWER

WHAT ARE EMOTIONS?   1 2 3 4 5 6 7 8 9 10   I'M A FEELINGS NINJA.

HOW WELL DO YOU COMMUNICATE YOUR OWN EMOTIONS?

DOES THIS MEAN I'M SUPPOSED TO TALK?   1 2 3 4 5 6 7 8 9 10   I AM ABLE TO ARTICULATE WHAT I FEEL VERBALLY ALONG WITH MY TONE AND POSTURE.

HOW WELL DO YOU CONNECT TO YOUR WIFE'S EMOTIONS?

SHE HAS FEELINGS?   1 2 3 4 5 6 7 8 9 10   SHE FEELS FELT.

SCORE YOUR ABILITY TO ENGAGE HER HEART, ESPECIALLY WHEN THERE ARE STRONG EMOTIONS.

I'M OUT.   1 2 3 4 5 6 7 8 9 10   I AM VERY RESILIENT & CAN HOLD HER PAIN.

QUESTIONS FOR HER

HOW WELL DOES YOUR HUSBAND CONNECT TO HIS OWN EMOTIONS?

1 2 3 4 5 6 7 8 9 10

HOW WELL DOES HE COMMUNICATE HIS OWN EMOTIONS?

1 2 3 4 5 6 7 8 9 10

HOW WELL DOES YOUR HUSBAND CONNECT TO YOUR EMOTIONS?

1 2 3 4 5 6 7 8 9 10

SCORE HIS ABILITY TO ENGAGE YOUR HEART, ESPECIALLY WHEN THERE ARE STRONG EMOTIONS.

1 2 3 4 5 6 7 8 9 10

QUESTIONS FOR HER

HOW WELL DO YOU CONNECT TO YOUR OWN EMOTIONS?

CIRCLE A NUMBER FOR YOUR ANSWER

WHAT ARE
EMOTIONS?
1 2 3 4 5 6 7 8 9 10
I'M A
FEELINGS
NINJA.

HOW WELL DO YOU COMMUNICATE YOUR OWN EMOTIONS?

DOES THIS
MEAN I'M
SUPPOSED
TO TALK?
1 2 3 4 5 6 7 8 9 10
I AM ABLE TO
ARTICULATE
WHAT I FEEL
VERBALLY
ALONG WITH
MY TONE AND
POSTURE.

HOW WELL DO YOU CONNECT TO YOUR HUSBAND'S EMOTIONS?

HE HAS
FEELINGS?
1 2 3 4 5 6 7 8 9 10
HE FEELS
FELT.

MSG

1 CORINTHIANS 13:12

We don't yet see things clearly. We're squinting in a fog, peering through a mist. But it won't be long before the weather clears and the sun shines bright! We'll see it all then, see it all as clearly as God sees us, knowing him directly just as he knows us!

PERSONAL REFLECTION

Remember that transparency is about intimacy. Deep intimacy means nothing obscured or hidden. What emotions stir as you consider one day we'll know God just as he knows us?

NEXT

On the next couple of pages, you'll see placeholders to transfer the sum of the scores from the previous pages. Take a moment to compare them, and see what the data tells you.

TOGETHER

THIS IS A CROSS BETWEEN THE NEWLYWED GAME AND
THE FAMILY FUED!

HOW WELL DO YOU CONNECT TO YOUR WIFE'S EMOTIONS?

SCORE YOUR ABILITY TO ENGAGE HER HEART, ESPECIALLY
WHEN THERE ARE STRONG EMOTIONS.

Discuss the scores. What do they tell you? If they are similar, why? If
not, why not? If the numbers don't align, what needs to happen to
change it?

TOGETHER

THIS IS A CROSS BETWEEN THE NEWLYWED GAME AND
THE FAMILY FUED!

HUSBANDS, HOW WELL DO YOU CONNECT TO YOUR OWN
EMOTIONS?

HUSBANDS, HOW WELL DO YOU COMMUNICATE YOUR OWN
EMOTIONS?

Discuss the scores. What do they tell you? If they are similar, why? If
not, why not? If the numbers don't align, what needs to happen to
change it?

QUESTION FOR BOTH

When you hear the word intimacy, what do you think of? What does that word mean to you? And has your definition changed along the healing journey?

QUESTIONS FOR HIM

What does it mean to you to be emotionally, intellectually and spiritually intimate with God?

Going back to the non-negotiable of spiritual commitment, you wrote about your spiritual journey to this point. How can you turn that into emotional, intellectual and spiritual intimacy with your wife? What would you share and how would you share it?

QUESTIONS FOR HIM

Do you practice emotional, intellectual and spiritual intimacy with other men? If so, describe what that looks like. If not, why not, and how can you go deeper with them?

QUESTIONS FOR HER

We don't want to make a list of to-do's or boxes to check, but can you give an example of what would be meaningful intimacy in each of these areas?

EMOTIONAL

Ex: I need to hear him explain and see his emotion about how hard this is for me.

INTELLECTUAL

Ex: I want to hear how he processes what happened when he was 12 and the impact of that on his story.

SPIRITUAL

Ex: I want to hear him pray for our kids more.

A NOTE ABOUT SAFETY

If you feel comfortable, please share these with him. Again, we aren't looking for a formula, but there is value in understanding what is meaningful to you, from your perspective, rather than making assumptions.

QUESTIONS FOR HER

What does it mean to you to be emotionally, intellectually and spiritually intimate with God?

PSALM 139:1-18

You have searched me, Lord,
    and you know me.
You know when I sit and when I rise;
    you perceive my thoughts from afar.
You discern my going out and my lying down;
    you are familiar with all my ways.
Before a word is on my tongue
    you, Lord, know it completely.
You hem me in behind and before,
    and you lay your hand upon me.
Such knowledge is too wonderful for me,
    too lofty for me to attain.
Where can I go from your Spirit?
    Where can I flee from your presence?
If I go up to the heavens, you are there;
    if I make my bed in the depths, you are there.
If I rise on the wings of the dawn,
    if I settle on the far side of the sea,
    even there your hand will guide me,
    your right hand will hold me fast.
If I say, "Surely the darkness will hide me
    and the light become night around me,"
    even the darkness will not be dark to you;
    the night will shine like the day,
    for darkness is as light to you.
For you created my inmost being;
    you knit me together in my mother's womb.

PSALM 139:1-18

I praise you because I am fearfully and wonderfully made;
    your works are wonderful,
    I know that full well.
My frame was not hidden from you
    when I was made in the secret place,
    when I was woven together in the depths of the earth.
Your eyes saw my unformed body;
    all the days ordained for me were written in your book
    before one of them came to be.
How precious to me are your thoughts, God!
    How vast is the sum of them!
Were I to count them,
    they would outnumber the grains of sand—
    when I awake, I am still with you.

PERSONAL REFLECTION

These verses give us a picture of both the intimacy and presence of God. Do you believe you could have a similar relationship with your spouse? One where nothing is hidden, there is a togetherness even when you're apart and you complete each others sentences because you know each other so well. Can you name ways that you could get closer to that today?

LEADERS GUIDE

#4

CONNECT WITH YOURSELF

6 FOUNDATIONS OF EFFECTIVE LEADING/FACILITATING

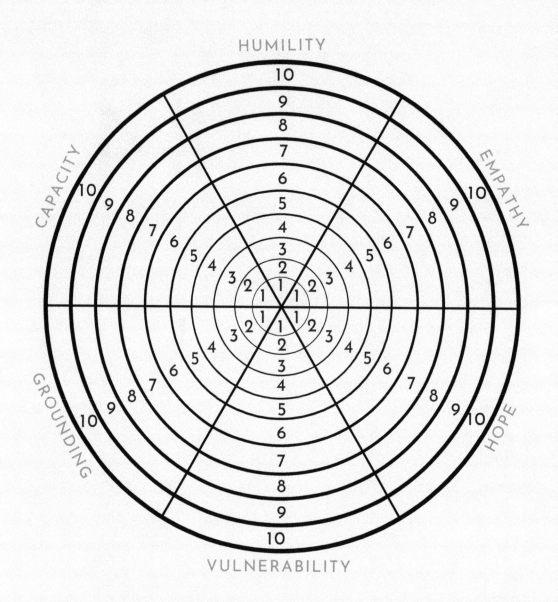

CONNECT WITH YOURSELF

What did the latest content stir in you emotionally? How do you feel about engaging the people you are helping with this content?

Was there anything this week in your personal story that makes engaging this material easier or more challenging? What and why?

CONNECT WITH YOURSELF

Are you passing any judgements or holding any narratives about the folks you are helping that could adversely impact your leadership and/or their experience? If so why and how can you relinquish or resolve those judgements or narratives?

CONNECT WITH THE FOLKS YOU'RE HELPING

What can you see in the material that uniquely connects to the their story? What questions might be helpful to ask based on that?

Where can you anticipate the discussion might get challenging and how can you prepare for that?

BIG PICTURE

KEY POINTS FOR THIS SECTION

Now is a really good time to remind husbands that if they remember anything not disclosed they should say it (assuming she has said she wants to know new info).

These non-negotiables are foundations not fixes.

Its easy to get caught up in the doing and it be disconnected from the heart.

Wives need a voice into these areas and their say matters. otherwise it will feel like something is forced on them.

WHAT TO WATCH FOR / BE AWARE OF

FOR HUSBANDS

■ His heart becoming disconnected from the work.
    1. Seeking affirmation for doing something different from her.

    2. His resistance to her needs, thoughts, and fears because they are different today than yesterday.

■ Open up a conversation about anything he might be resistant to engage radical honesty in.

FOR WIVES

■ Minimizing or downplaying her own needs.
    1. Seeing the work required in the non-negotiables as "too much" or feeling needy by asking him to implement the non-negotiables.

continued...

BIG PICTURE

WHAT TO WATCH FOR / BE AWARE OF

FOR WIVES

2. Seeing her settle for him not implementing the non negotiables and brushing it off or making excuses for him.

■ Remind her that her needs might change over the course of this process and that's ok! It doesn't make her needy, unrealistic or requiring too much of him.

■ Her changing needs don't make her crazy!

O5

NON-NEGOTIABLES
PART 2

NON-NEGOTIABLES PART 2

Accountability isn't about what someone else does. It's about what we do.

ACCOUNTABILITY

Accountability in the trust-building process is certainly a non-negotiable. Unfortunately, it is frequently both misunderstood and misapplied. Sometimes accountability or an accountability group is confused with being a good ol' boys club. It's where guys sit around replaying and romanticizing their escapades while slapping each other on the back. It seems like they all have a disregard for their wives and "what happens in group stays in group". That's not helpful.

Alternatively, swinging the pendulum the complete opposite direction, it can be militaristic in nature. It's the place they go to pay penance. Where there's an angry sponsor or mentor who will firmly reprimand and punish a man who doesn't do his homework that week. Also not helpful.

A third misconception is that it is simply a safe place to land. An accountability partner or group is a place to find encouragement and friendship, without challenge or judgement, but there is really no drive to do or be better. Again, not helpful.

So what is helpful?

Accountability isn't about what someone else does. It is about what we do. It is really about intimacy. It is about the posture of our own heart, and our willingness to be known. Known in what we are doing and who we are, known in what we aren't doing and who we are not, and known in what we will do and who we will become.

ACCOUNTABILITY

With this in mind, what is helpful is to have men in our life who will be curious when we're not living as we desire, who will challenge us to grow and change, who will celebrate with us when we do, who will hold our wives in high esteem, who will not tolerate mediocrity and who will give us courage to return to the battle repeatedly.

We want accountability to help us become all that God is calling us to be and to help us live out of that. It should help us move forward, not just keep us from slipping backward.

QUESTIONS FOR HIM

does your accountability system operate as just described? Or is it one of the unhealthy dynamics (boys club, militaristic, soft place to land)? Describe how and why.

Name something you need to do to improve the accountability relationships in your life. How do you need to engage differently for you to get more out of it? How do you need to engage differently so that someone else gets more out of it?

QUESTIONS FOR HIM

What are the 3 main things you need to be accountable for today and why?

01

WHAT:

WHY:

02

WHAT:

WHY:

03

WHAT:

WHY:

QUESTIONS FOR HER

How do you feel about his accountability relationships currently? Do they add security? Do they feel like one of the unhealthy groups mentioned? Describe why.

What could change, if anything, in his accountability relationships that would help you feel more secure and thus more likely to trust?

QUESTIONS FOR HER

What might you need to be accountable for with your support system?

PROVERBS 13:20 & 1 CORINTHIANS 15:33

Walk with the wise and become wise,
   for a companion of fools suffers harm.

Do not be misled: "Bad company corrupts good character."

PERSONAL REFLECTION

Accountability puts our heart in a posture of humility and in a position to become wise with good character. What does wisdom and good character mean to you?

NON-NEGOTIABLES PART 2

We are not trying to operate by the "don'ts". We are trying to operate by the "instead-ofs".

COMPUTER & INTERNET

Our time online matters. Whether or not your integrity issues included using the internet for sketchy reasons, how you navigate life online can be a big boost to trust building. There is an opportunity to show our wives where our priorities are, and to reassure them through our willingness to surrender some aspects of our online life.

I want to remind you that the principle here isn't restriction. We are not trying to operate by the "don'ts". We are trying to operate by the "instead-ofs". Meaning, we want to invest in ourselves instead of investing time online. Instead of aimlessly surfing or reading news, or watching entertainment we invest our time reading helpful books, having more meaningful conversations and doing work that is oriented towards changing our minds, hearts and character.

The other thing that comes into play here is that some wives don't want to feel like a parent or a nag, so they sacrifice their own security with silence. They feel anxiety when their husband has his phone in his hand; but they don't want to have to say, "what are you doing" or "I wish you weren't on your phone all the time". It may be as innocuous as checking scores or fantasy sports updates, looking at the weather or mapping out a vacation, but she can't know that for sure. So the anxiety and fear are there, even if low-level.

When we limit ourselves and invest our time elsewhere instead of online, we are helping offset that anxiety. We rebuild trust when we mitigate her fear without her having to ask. And what we see is that wives respect their husbands more when they see him investing in his own recovery because they know they'll ultimately benefit. The two will become a better one.

QUESTIONS FOR HIM

Do you and your wife have differing opinions of what your online life needs to look like? Are there requests she's made that you have been resistant to? If so, how and why?

Is there resistance within you about reducing or changing how you spend your time online. If so, why? If not, why not?

QUESTIONS FOR HIM

What aspects of your online life are a necessity and how can you provide reassurance around them?

Email	I can review my email correspondence (including sent and trash) with my wife every 48 hours.

A NOTE ABOUT REASSURANCE

Don't confuse providing her reassurance with an authoritarian relationship. This isn't about reporting to mom or the parole officer about our behavior. This about bringing her into our world (specifically online) to show her she doesn't have to be fearful and that she's not crazy. We aren't doing this to stay out of trouble, we are doing this to create security, which will lead to trust.

QUESTIONS FOR HER

What aspects of his online life make you uneasy, distrustful or outright angry and why?

Describe how you experience his response to limiting or changing the way he does life online. Do you sense humility and willingess? Resistance or indignance? Also describe how his response makes you feel.

COMPUTER & INTERNET

For some wives, there's just nothing that provides reassurance relative to his online life. He can go through his email with her, but she always questions what he deleted. He can reduce the number of connections he has on any social media platform, regardless of professionalism, and yet some of them will still be triggering. He can have filtering and monitoring software installed, but there's a looming skepticism that he's tech saavy enough to get around it. There's just no foolproof way to provide reassurance online.

For wives what this means is that the only thing she can rely on is the texture of her husband's engagement around this area. If there is humility, willingness, and a sense of contrition it will provide some security. A husband's agency in this area matters too. That means its not just a wife saying delete this or stay off that, but a husband managing himself, determining that there are areas of online life that are dangerous, not God honoring, or simply that just aren't beneficial. The texture we're talking about also includes attitude. Is there resentment and exasperation to having to change life online? That'll only serve to create more insecurity. For husbands, we have to look at this as an opportunity, not a consequence.

Having said all that, some folks are looking for filtering and monitoring software. Here are a few resources to that end.

SOFTWARE

COVENANT EYES	EVER ACCOUNTABLE

Covenant Eyes has been around the longest and is certainly the largest filtering and monitoring software available.

EverAccountable provides monitoring but not filtering. I've talked extensively with their CEO and I can vouch that they are passionate about technology and helping people.

ACCOUNTABLE2YOU	BARK

While I don't have first hand experience with this one, I've known several clients who trust it.

Specifically labeled as a parental control, it can be very beneficial and I have clients who trust it.

PROVERBS 22:3

The prudent see danger and take refuge,
    but the simple keep going and pay the penalty.

PERSONAL REFLECTION

What does it mean to you to "see danger and take refuge" with respect to our online world? If we 'keep going' as the verse says, what penalty will be paid and by whom (specifically name all the people you can see directly impacted)?

NON-
NEGOTIABLES
PART 1

THE WORKPLACE

Meaningful work is important. So is doing meaningful work well, with integrity. Keep in mind though, that meaningful work done well cannot trump a safe, intimate marriage. Too frequently we talk to men who describe aspects of their work that create insecurity and jeopardize their integrity as "just the way things are". Here are a few examples:

- Telling white lies to expedite a sale.
- Dinner or the golf course with drinks is how you close.
- A female assistant because they're the only ones applying for the job.
- Closed door, 1-1 meetings.
- "Team culture" means sharing your personal lives.

Of course there are realities at work that we all have to contend with. But, it seems that we too easily accept them as the default rather than challenge them for the sake of 1) our integrity and 2) our wife's sense of security. Do you really have to staff the trade show? Do 1-1 meetings with the opposite sex really make sense, or would it actually be better on the company's behalf to have 3 people in any meeting like that? False scarcity may close a deal, but will you really get demoted or fired, or will y'all go hungry if you miss your quota? Sometimes, the company culture and an overbearing manager dictates how it will be. Then we have to decide if that's ok for our journey. It may mean we need to have awkward conversations with our boss to tweak things. We might need to be the odd man out when it comes to the team environment. Or we may need to find a new job or career entirely!

We can't stress enough that these decisions around the work environment need to be influenced first and foremost by what God is calling you to. It has to be a question of your integrity. Can you be the man God is calling you to be in this professional environment, as it currently operates?

QUESTIONS FOR HIM

What defaults at work do you need to challenge and what questions need to be asked as a result (of yourself, of coworkers, of a boss or employees)?

What needs to change in the way you conduct yourself professionally? Please be specific and describe how you can make the necessary changes.

Do you feel resistance to changing the way you operate professionally? If so why? If not, why not?

QUESTIONS FOR HIM

What steps can you take to provide your wife more reassurance while you're at work? Do you resent having to do that? If so, why? If not, why not?

Is your current work environment conducive to redemption? Have you ever looked at it through this lens? If so, why? If not, why not?

QUESTIONS FOR HIM

Are you willing to find a new job, and possibly a new career, if that's what it takes? If yes, why? If not, why not?

QUESTIONS FOR HER

What defaults in your husband's work environment need to be challenged and why?

What aspects of your husband's professional life cause fear or anxiety and why?

QUESTIONS FOR HER

Sometimes husbands work in triggering environments or with specifically triggering people. Are there any boundaries you need him to set in the workplace to help you feel safer?

Wives as well sometimes work in triggering environments or with specifically triggering people. Are there any boundaries you need in your own workplace (this includes home!) to help you feel safer?

PROVERBS 28:6 & PROVERBS 22:1

Better the poor whose walk is blameless
   than the rich whose ways are perverse.

A good name is more desirable than great riches;
   to be esteemed is better than silver or gold.

PERSONAL REFLECTION

What does a blameless walk and good name mean to you? And how do you live in a way professionally to achieve both of them? Also, is a good name really better than riches to you?

NON-
NEGOTIABLES
PART 1

I never want you to regret that you stayed.

RESTITUTION

Restitution isn't a punishment. Many men in the office often think about this as the penalty they must pay to their wives for betrayal. Like it's the perpetual, proverbial doghouse they will always live in. That is sad, because it couldn't be farther from the truth.

We need to view restitution through a God lens. A biblical word study will bring up several different definitions, but the two that apply to our use of the word are:

1) to be at peace with

2) to repay or restore

To see how restitution and peace are connected, it is helpful to note that Hebrew word for restitution is the root of the word Shalom. You've probably heard that before. Shalom means peace; but the essence of the word is less about the absence of war or conflict, and more about the idea of things being the way they were intended. That things would be at peace; what God had in mind originally. It means to be complete and full, as it should be. Hold on to that for a minute...

To repay or restore in this context means to make whole, to compensate for a thing lost. The wholeness that was lost was the ideal or fullness that God had in mind. To illustrate, Joel 2:25 tells us, "I will repay you for the years the locusts have eaten..." The notion therein is that God will not only give them what He intends for them to have today, but will compensate them for

RESTITUTION

what they lost along the way. He'll restore the fullness or wholeness that He originally imagined and designed for them.

Now we'll connect the two dots. Think of restitution as striving to restore your marriage, and her life specifically, to the fullness that it was intended to be; the way God imagined and designed it. What a sweet opportunity to live into!

Not punishment or penalty, but possibility. We get to try and make her life what it should've been when God handed us the baton to care for her in the first place. We urge you, as a husband, to look at this as what we get to do, not what we have to do. If you experience reluctance and resistance to this idea, it might be an indicator of how uphill your process is going to be, unfortunately.

QUESTIONS FOR HIM

How do you view restitution? Is it a lifelong sentence or is it a privileged opportunity and why?

In what ways can you see the possibility of making her life whole and as God intended it? Perhaps it has to do with things beyond the marriage like money, hobbies, parenting, career.

QUESTIONS FOR HIM

What do you think and feel when you consider that she can have a new marriage to a new man that looks the same and has the same name as you?

In what areas would you like to see a repayment of "the years the locusts have eaten" in your own life and why?

QUESTIONS FOR HER

What do you think and feel when you consider restitution?

Do you believe your husband can see this as possibility rather than punishment? If so, why? If not, why not?

In what areas would you like to see a repayment of "the years the locusts have eaten" and why?

QUESTIONS FOR HER

Are there some areas that today seem like they could never be repaired, repaid or redeemed in your life or in y'alls relationship? What areas and why?

LUKE 19:8

But Zacchaeus stood up and said to the Lord, "Look, Lord! Here and now I give half of my possessions to the poor, and if I have cheated anybody out of anything, I will pay back four times the amount."

PERSONAL REFLECTION

Zacchaeus paid the people he cheated restitution; by 4x! Do you see this as his punishment and penance, or as his opportunity to restore what has been lost in the lives of those people and why?

Husbands, take a second and imagine being on the receiving end of Zack's call. He dials you up and says, "hey, I cheated you out of that money and I'm sorry for what I did, and I'm sorry for the pain it caused you. I'm paying you back 4 times that amount". What do you feel and why?

PAUSE

We want to take a time out here. We've covered heavy stuff. Painful topics. This is no easy task. So, take another break and breathe. Remember, this is a chance to process your experience at the moment. Then we'll get to the next section.

Remember that grieving is making sense of our story.

GRIEVING FOR WIVES

Remember that grieving is part of the process. You can think of grieving as 'making sense of my story'. Grieving is cyclical and iterative; it doesn't happen in one fell swoop. You have to cycle through it, revisiting some aspects of the betrayal multiple times (unfortunately). Four of the big stages of grief and examples of them are: Denial - I can't believe this is my life. Anger - I'm rightfully enraged about what has happened. Bargaining - negotiating with myself to try and stop the pain. And finally, Hopelessness - feeling despair and disbelief that things can change or be healed. All these stages are normal. Some last longer than others, and they can change on a dime (which is also normal).

Take a moment, identify and write down where you see these aspects of grief in your process right now.

DENIAL

Ex: "I don't want to believe all the ways this impacts me."

ANGER

Ex: "I'm furious that I gave up my career to support his dreams while he lived a double life."

GRIEVING FOR WIVES
CONTINUED

BARGAINING

Ex: "At this point if he doesn't do recovery perfectly I'm leaving."

HOPELESSNESS

Ex: "I'll always be unstable and angry."

As a wife, you're not crazy! You might be on the emotional crazy coaster, but you aren't crazy. You're grieving. When you feel your emotions change on a dime, love turn to hate, to a puddle on the floor, to just plain numb, remember that its normal. You'll get through this, and you'll get off the roller coaster. It won't last forever!

GRIEVING FOR HUSBANDS

Remember that grieving is part of the process. You can think of grieving as 'making sense of my story'. Grieving is cyclical and iterative; it doesn't happen in one fell swoop. You have to cycle through it, revisiting some aspects of the betrayal multiple times (unfortunately) as well as aspects of your acting out. Not in a way that relishes or romanticizes it, but in a way that sheds truth and light on just how dark it is.

Four of the big stages of grief along with examples are: Denial - I can't believe this is my life, I can't believe what I've done. Anger - I'm rightfully enraged about what I've done. Bargaining - negotiating with myself to try and stop the pain, to try to and figure out a way to salvage things. And finally, Hopelessness - feeling despair and disbelief that things can change or be healed. Just as for wives, these are all normal. They come in waves, and it won't last forever.

Take a moment, identify and write down where you see these aspects of grief in your process right now.

DENIAL

Ex: "This only impacts a couple areas of life, not everything."

ANGER

Ex: "I'm angry that she won't own her part in our marriage issues."

BARGAINING

Ex: "God if you fix this I'll become a missionary."

HOPELESSNESS

Ex: "Our marriage was doomed since day 1."

LEADERS GUIDE

#5

#1 CONNECT WITH YOURSELF

6 FOUNDATIONS OF EFFECTIVE LEADING/FACILITATING

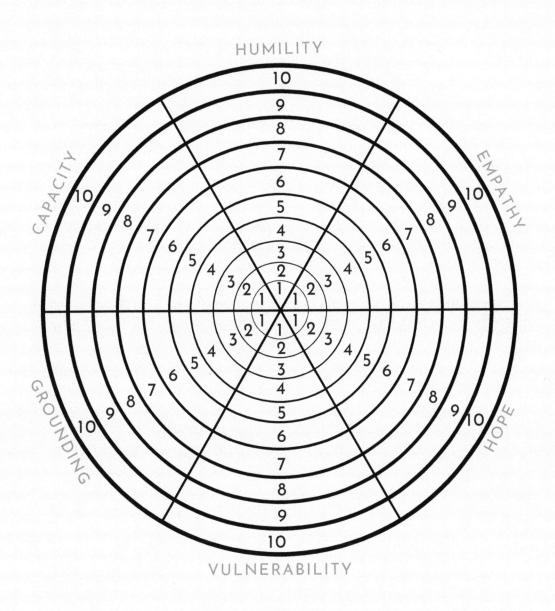

CONNECT WITH YOURSELF

What did the latest content stir in you emotionally? How do you feel about engaging the people you are helping with this content?

Was there anything this week in your personal story that makes engaging this material easier or more challenging? What and why?

CONNECT WITH YOURSELF

Are you passing any judgements or holding any narratives about the folks you are helping that could adversely impact your leadership and/or their experience? If so why and how can you relinquish or resolve those judgements or narratives?

CONNECT WITH THE FOLKS YOU'RE HELPING

What can you see in the material that uniquely connects to the their story? What questions might be helpful to ask based on that?

Where can you anticipate the discussion might get challenging and how can you prepare for that?

BIG PICTURE

KEY POINTS FOR THIS SECTION

Trust is destroyed at her expense and is rebuilt at his.

The non-negotiables, in most cases, are a major change in the way spouses operate and communicate. The non-negotiables foundationally give insight to the areas where the sexual betrayal was rampant because trust and freedom were abused. This is a call to a different kind of living.

WHAT TO WATCH FOR / BE AWARE OF

FOR HUSBANDS

- Excuses, resistance or rationalization for why these can't be implemented.

    1. Resisting accountability partners because he is embarrassed or doesn't have anyone in his life that can be safe accountability for him. Need to see willingness to risk with someone who seems safe.

    2. Building a case to not have accountability software on his devices. Ex. "I can't use the internet for work the way I need to with this filter on it" or "It's really cumbersome and slow to use the accountability software browser."

    3. Generalization of his workday with no detail. He should be very specific around his interactions and time spent at work should be explained with clarity.

    4. Holding on to his freedom and privacy or looking for equanimity around her phone, email, etc.

#3   BIG PICTURE

WHAT TO WATCH FOR / BE AWARE OF

FOR WIVES

▪ Her feeling embarrassed or controlling for wanting to be integrated into his life.

   1. She should have access to his accountability guys so she can ask questions to get a sense of security.

   2. Because of the broken trust, it is important to understand how he is behaving on devices and around other people when she's not around him. She shouldn't be ashamed of this need.

   3. This is the space where a wife needs the freedom to feel. He should be working to cultivate safety emotionally while she is grieving and letting out her emotions via questions, inquiries, or anger.

▪ Her feeling like a parent who has to monitor her child while he's grounded. We want him to own helping her feel a sense of reassurance, not her feeling like a parent and him a child.

▪ Her processing restitution and forgiveness. Encouraging her that desiring restitution isn't a contradiction to forgiveness.

06

EMPATHY & AMENDS

EMPATHY

OUR ABILITY TO CONNECT WITH AND COMMUNICATE ABOUT OUR WIFE'S PAIN

The ability to feel our wife's pain and let them know they are seen and heard is really challenging for some of us. Especially when we are swirling in shame or feeling overwhelmed by regret and hopelessness. Our tendency is to defend, deflect and shut down, which of course just makes them feel even more unseen and unheard. It can be a vicious cycle. But it can also stop!

For most men the feelings are in there. The tenderness, compassion and protectiveness is inside them, they just don't know how to access it and articulate it. That takes work and practice, which is part of the design of the Amends Matrix.

As with anything where we desire mastery, it takes practice. It takes work and energy and effort outside the moments when we need it. Professional athletes can't just show up on gameday and expect to perform at their highest level. Writers can't just write when they feel like it and expect to produce a worthwhile read. Artists can't just paint or draw when they have a stroke of genius. Such is the case for us.

We can't expect to be compassionate and empathetic when our wives are standing in front of us in pain, anger and hopelessness if we haven't actually been practicing connecting to those emotions outside the moment.

This section is meant to help with practice.

EMPATHY & AMENDS

When there's
nothing left to do,
nothing left to say,
what matters most
is how you'll be.

EMPATHY

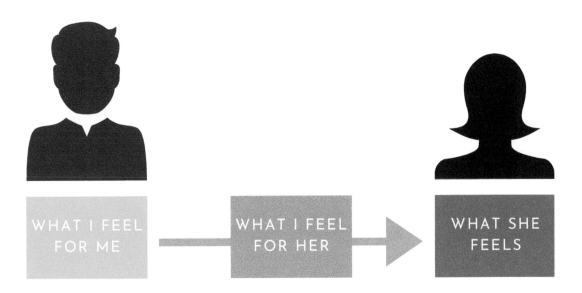

| WHAT I FEEL FOR ME | WHAT I FEEL FOR HER | → | WHAT SHE FEELS |

It is important for us to be able to acknowledge what we feel and how we are impacted by our situations and experiences. Equally important is to be able to conceptualize and identify what she feels and her experience, given the totality of her story.

For so many wives, empathy is really an experience of feeling felt, where a husband steps beyond his own pain, into hers. Often the missing link in her experiencing empathy is his inability to express what he feels for her. Most husbands genuinely feel heartbreak for their wive's broken heart, and they would give anything to take back the hurt, but they have difficulty articulating it. True empathy comes across the wire when it shows on our face, comes through in our words and tone, and is expressed in our actions.

A NOTE ABOUT EMPATHY

For many men the empathy muscle is weak. We've been self-focused for a long time and feeling someone else's pain isn't something we are good at. Good news though; empathy can be learned! That muscle can get strengthened. I say this because sometimes wives feel like their husband is a hopeless case when he is stoic or self-focused in the face of her pain. But it can actually be developed.
For more help with empathy please consider taking our Empathy Masterclass. www.redemptiveliving.com/empathy

QUESTIONS FOR HIM

What are you fearful of with bringing up the past? What are you afraid to feel? What are you afraid she'll feel? What are you afraid will happen relationally?

Think about your family of origin for a moment and consider how the past was talked about. Or was it? What was caught or taught about brining up past pain?

QUESTIONS FOR HIM

What are the excuses you use (or used in the past) to avoid bringing up painful things from y'alls story? Did the excuses blame her? How will you fight blaming her going forward?

Describe a time recently when you responded to your wife from a place of "what I feel for her", rather than "what I feel for me". How was the experience different for you? For her?

QUESTIONS FOR HIM

Remember that we are living the sum total of our story today. How well do you know your wife's story? Explain how you can see the sum total of her story coming to bear on today..

How would you define empathy? How is it different than sympathy? What can be a clue that you're expressing sympathy and needing to shift to empathy?

QUESTIONS FOR HIM

SCORE YOURSELF ON EMPATHY - HOW WELL DO YOU DO IT?

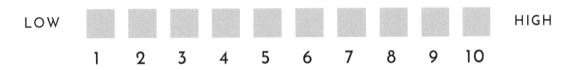

LOW   1   2   3   4   5   6   7   8   9   10   HIGH

Take a moment and practice - when you think of her story, including your betrayal, what do you <u>feel for her</u>?

Now take another look at what you wrote above. Is it really what you feel for her? Or is it what you feel about you? Or what she feels? Invite her feedback on it.

QUESTIONS FOR HER

SCORE YOUR HUSBAND ON EMPATHY - HOW WELL DOES HE DO IT?

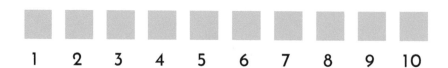

1   2   3   4   5   6   7   8   9   10

What would you say is missing or needs to be upgraded in the way he connects to your emotions and communicates how he feels for you?

What specific aspects of betrayal do you feel like you need more empathy on right now?

QUESTIONS FOR HER

Are you fearful of bringing up the past? If so, why? If not, why not?

The past pain isn't just about betrayal, it includes the other aspects of the relationship that have been hurtful. What other aspects need to be addressed, if not now, at some point, in order to find healing and redemption?

ROMANS 12:15 & JOHN 11:33

Rejoice with those who rejoice; mourn with those who mourn.

When Jesus saw her weeping, and the Jews who had come along with her also weeping, he was deeply moved in spirit and troubled.

PERSONAL REFLECTION

We have a god of emotions and of empathy. Jesus modeled it and through the Holy Spirit we can develop it.

Husbands, write out a prayer asking god to give you a heart of empathy like his.

Wives, are there aspects of your husband's story that you feel empathy for today? If so what and why?

EMPATHY & AMENDS

MAKING AMENDS

NOT JUST CLEANING UP OUR SIDE OF THE
STREET, BUT ALSO CLEANING UP ALL THE JUNK
WE THREW ON HER SIDE

Let's take a minute and give context for Amends and the Amends Matrix. First, we need to talk about what it is not. It's not a quick fix or a band-aid; simply walking through an amends doesn't take the pain away. It's also not a tool to manipulate the emotional outcome; sometimes men use it expecting it'll make their wives happy and there will be less anger. It's also not a one-and-done type punch card; as if we talked about that painful topic so now we never have to again.

Amends and using the Amends Matrix are really about love, care, compassion and empathy, as we just discussed. It's a way to care for our wives and give them some indication that we are understanding the pain we've caused, while also giving them a glimmer of hope for a better future. Don't get that confused; this isn't a way of getting

kudos or proving that we are different. That's making it about us. We want to keep the focus on them.

For wives, this isn't meant to make you feel better (even though sometimes it might). We want you to hear your husband walk through this in a way that you sense his sincerity and have a window into where his head and heart are. Some of the words might make you mad and some of the explanations may sound like excuses. But even with that, we want you to get a feel for the texture of his engagement.

We tell men in the office it's ok if they fumble the words, stutter, and have to read off their page; as long as their heart of compassion shows through. And that happens via the texture of it.

MAKING AMENDS

AMENDS MATRIX COMPARED TO 12-STEP AMENDS

There is an important distinction we need to make here. Sometimes making amends in this context gets confused with Steps 8 & 9 in the 12-steps. Those are great steps and we have personally done them! But this amend making is different.

First, stepwork amends is about righting our wrongs. We acknowledge we hurt people and apologize for it, owning it humbly and thoroughly. But, generally speaking, we don't give backstory and we don't go into the other person's pain.

When using the Amends Matrix, we are very intentionally speaking to the backstory and also engaging the other person's (our wives) pain. We are doing an empathy deep-dive!

Second, stepwork amends has a philosophical bent that says I am cleaning up my side of the street, but that's where my responsibility ends. Amends making, as we are doing it in this course, says we go beyond our side of the street, and clean up all the junk we threw on the other person's side of the street. Going farther, we clean up some of their mess too, even if it wasn't ours. Not because we're co-dependent, but because we love.

This is the essence of what Jesus did. He cleaned up a mess that wasn't his so the people whose mess it was could live in redemption.

AMENDS MATRIX

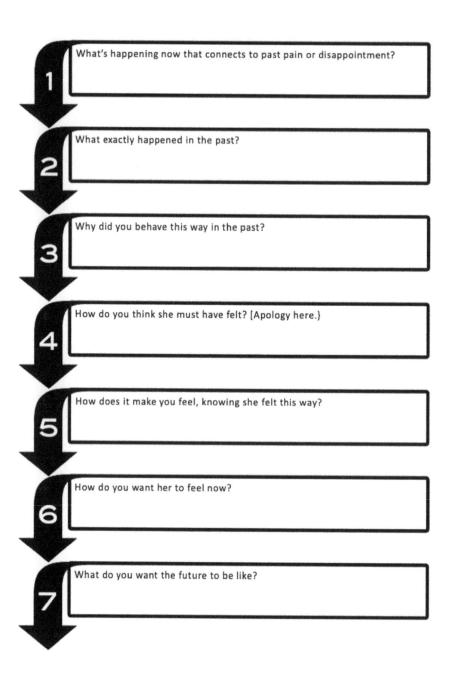

1. What's happening now that connects to past pain or disappointment?

2. What exactly happened in the past?

3. Why did you behave this way in the past?

4. How do you think she must have felt? [Apology here.]

5. How does it make you feel, knowing she felt this way?

6. How do you want her to feel now?

7. What do you want the future to be like?

QUESTIONS FOR HIM

How do you feel about engaging amends? If there is fear, what is driving it? What do you hope will come out of it?

Regarding step 3 in the matrix, do you feel confident you can describe the why behind the what today? Can you go beyond the superficial answers? If so, why? If not, why not?

AMENDS LIST – HUSBANDS

IDENTIFYING PAST PAIN

Use the space below to identify points of past pain; things that are amendable. It may be a particular moment or instance, a theme or a systemic issue that is longstanding in your character or relationship. Don't think about this as "all the ways I've messed up or failed", instead think of this as "all the areas we have a chance to find healing in".

I checked out emotionally when our son was born.

I dismissed your intuition over and over again.

I belittled you when you tried to ask questions about my spiritual life.

QUESTIONS FOR HER

How well does he know your story? Both the parts that preceded him and your time together. Does he know the deepest wounds you've experienced outside of him?

At this point, what do you feel when you hear the words "I'm sorry", and why?

QUESTIONS FOR HER

How do you feel about him engaging you with the amends matrix?
Does it sound helpful or hurtful? Meaningful or a waste of time?

Can you see it being meaningful even if it sounds somewhat contrived?

AMENDS LIST – WIVES

IDENTIFYING PAST PAIN

Use the space below to identify points of past pain; things that are amendable. These are things that you know it would be meaningful to hear him sincerely address. It may be a particular moment or instance, a theme or a systemic issue that is longstanding in your relationship.

You didn't give me a choice at our engagement.

You dismissed my intuition.

Not reaching our retirement goas because we have to spend money on recovery.

PROVERBS 14:9

Fools mock at making amends for sin,
    but goodwill is found among the upright.

PERSONAL REFLECTION

Making amends for sin is ancient. The benefit is both to the sinner and sinned against. Goodwill and favor are available to someone humble enough to make amends. What do goodwill and favor mean to you?

#6

LEADERS GUIDE

#1 CONNECT WITH YOURSELF

6 FOUNDATIONS OF EFFECTIVE LEADING/FACILITATING

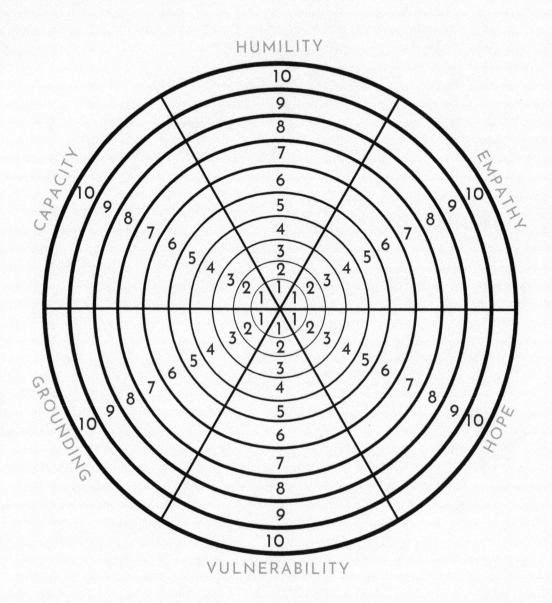

CONNECT WITH YOURSELF

What did the latest content stir in you emotionally? How do you feel about engaging the people you are helping with this content?

Was there anything this week in your personal story that makes engaging this material easier or more challenging? What and why?

#1 ## CONNECT WITH YOURSELF

Are you passing any judgements or holding any narratives about the folks you are helping that could adversely impact your leadership and/or their experience? If so why and how can you relinquish or resolve those judgements or narratives?

CONNECT WITH THE FOLKS YOU'RE HELPING

What can you see in the material that uniquely connects to the their story? What questions might be helpful to ask based on that?

Where can you anticipate the discussion might get challenging and how can you prepare for that?

#3   BIG PICTURE

KEY POINTS FOR THIS SECTION

If necessary, discuss the differences between a 12 step amends and the trust building amends process.

Tee-up couples to adopt the amends process through the matrix provided.

Intimacy is created through empathy in past pain, as it is experienced in the present, and can be a healing moment for a new future.

WHAT TO WATCH FOR / BE AWARE OF

FOR HUSBANDS

- ■ Resistance or insecurity impeding empathy.
    1. Inauthenticity and going through the motions without being connected emotionally to her pain.

    2. Resistance to the process from his own insecurities or pride that might have him winging the conversation without having done the proper preparation, thus furthering damage.

- ■ One and done thinking.
    1. Buying into the idea that once an amends has been done, it won't ever come up again. "We talked about that once, so why do we have to talk about it again?"

continued...

#3   BIG PICTURE

WHAT TO WATCH FOR / BE AWARE OF

FOR WIVES

- Make sure she is ready emotionally to go through the amends process.

    1, Sometimes early on in a couples journey doing amends work opens a wound is too soon. So be careful not to apply pressure for her to be ready just because that's where you are in the curriculum.

- Sometimes as leaders we have to highlight his effort even if the outcome of an amends is wonky, awkward or painful. He did the work; maybe not well, but his heart was in it and he didn't shy away from it.

07

TACTICAL

TACTICAL

TOOLS IN YOUR TOOLBELT

The tactical section reviews and highlights a handful of tools to rebuild trust. With anything we're building, different tools at different times are needed to be effective. Sometimes you can hammer with a screwdriver, and sometimes you need a sledgehammer. At times you can pull a nail with pliers, and sometimes you need a crowbar. The point here is these tools are suggestions, and as you use them you'll find out whether they are right for the job at the time.

In addition, for husbands, we have to remember 2 important pieces. First, that these tools aren't just boxes to check. We're not expecting the tasks themselves to rebuild the trust. Just because we do the thing doesn't mean it guarantees the outcome. If it becomes about checking the box it will hurt your process.

Second, the way you keep it from being a to-do list is by keeping your heart connected to it. Consistently coming back to the reality that betrayal has degraded her dignity and fear is ever present will help us stay connected to our hearts. These tools are motivated by empathy.

For wives, we want these to make a difference. If any of them sound ridiculous or more hurtful than helpful please say so. If you have something different in mind, say that too! We want you to have what you need. As you watch him utilize the tools, there may be times where it seems like box-checking. Call it if you see it! If it's actually not box-checking inside him, you should get a humble response from him.

TACTICAL

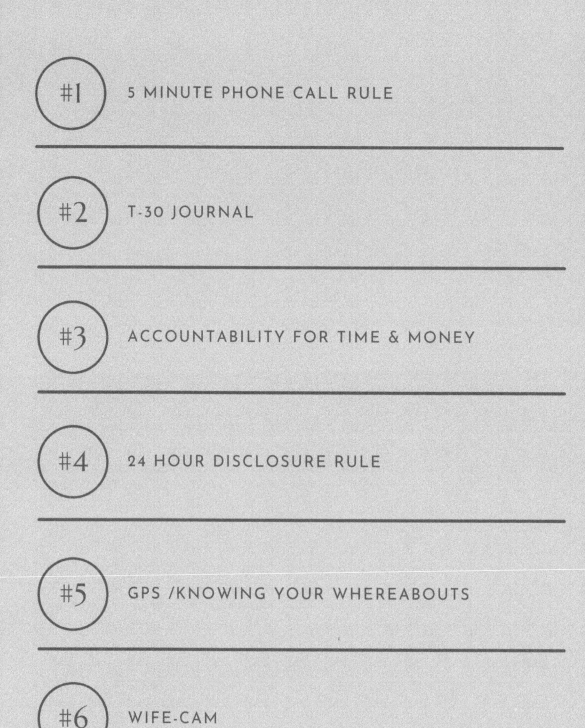

#1 5 MINUTE PHONE CALL RULE

#2 T-30 JOURNAL

#3 ACCOUNTABILITY FOR TIME & MONEY

#4 24 HOUR DISCLOSURE RULE

#5 GPS /KNOWING YOUR WHEREABOUTS

#6 WIFE-CAM

You can't prove what you're not doing wrong, you can only prove what you are doing right.

QUESTIONS FOR HIM

Of the 6 tactical ways to increase security, which would be the hardest for you to implement and why?

Are there any tactics described in this section that you feel are impossible to implement? If so, why? If not, why not?

QUESTIONS FOR HIM

Effort / Heart / Consistency are required to rebuild trust and create security. Describe your level of commitment to these today. Give examples of where/how your wife would see them.

Think about and name 2 more tactics that you can try and implement to rebuild trust. Then talk with your wife about them to get her input.

O1

O2

QUESTIONS FOR HIM

Are you sitting on anything......anything...that you know you need to tell her?

QUESTIONS FOR HER

Are there any of the tactical suggestions outlined in this session that you feel would not be helpful? if so why? What would need to be tweaked to provide you the most security possible?

Will you elaborate on any other ways your husband can tactically increase emotional security?

QUESTIONS FOR HER

You, as a wife, should have full veto power on all things related to trust building and recovery. Do you feel your husband honors your voice on this? If so, how? If not, why not?

PROVERBS 16:9

In their hearts humans plan their course,
  but the Lord establishes their steps.

PERSONAL REFLECTION

Husbands, as you consider implementing the tactical tools as part of your plan, invite God into it. Write a prayer that could be your daily invitation for him to establish your steps.

Wives, write a prayer asking the Lord to establish your steps as you plan your course.

PAUSE

This is the last time out to take inventory of grief. Remember, for both husband and wife, the grieving won't be so heavy, so intense, or difficult forever. As you process through the grief, it will dissipate.

Remember that grieving is making sense of our story.

GRIEVING FOR WIVES

Take a moment, identify and write down where you see these aspects of grief in your process right now.

DENIAL

Ex: "It's all too much. I just want to be normal."

ANGER

Ex: "I feel rage that I was duped."

BARGAINING

Ex: "I'm too embarrassed to tell anyone so I'll just put on a happy face when we're around people."

HOPELESSNESS

Ex: "This disqualifies us from so many aspects of life."

As a wife, you're not crazy! You might be on the emotional crazy coaster, but you aren't crazy. You're grieving. When you feel your emotions change on a dime, love turn to hate„ to a puddle on the floor, to just plain numb, remember that its normal. You'll get through this, and you'll get off the roller coaster. It won't last forever!

GRIEVING FOR HUSBANDS

Take a moment, identify and write down where you see these aspects of grief in your process right now.

Ex: "It's all too much. I just want to be normal."

Ex: "I'm angry that at this point in our life this is the focus."

GRIEVING FOR HUSBANDS
CONTINUED

BARGAINING

Ex: "I may be messed up but I'll make sure my kids aren't."

HOPELESSNESS

Ex: "I don't think I'm capable of all that's required to fix this."

LEADERS GUIDE

#7

#1 CONNECT WITH YOURSELF

6 FOUNDATIONS OF EFFECTIVE
LEADING/FACILITATING

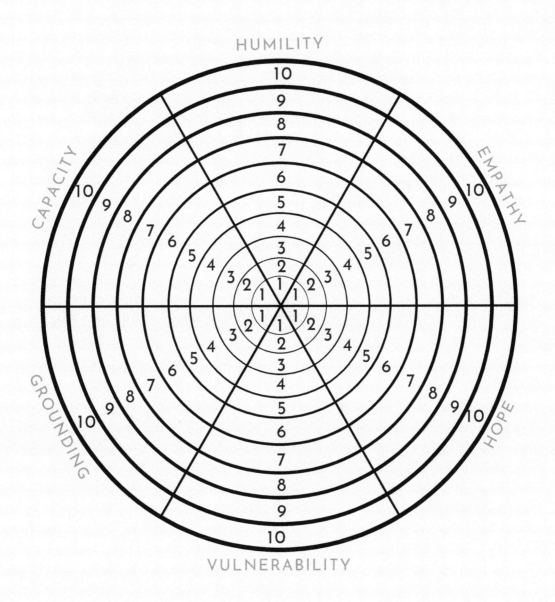

CONNECT WITH YOURSELF

What did the latest content stir in you emotionally? How do you feel about engaging the people you are helping with this content?

Was there anything this week in your personal story that makes engaging this material easier or more challenging? What and why?

CONNECT WITH YOURSELF

Are you passing any judgements or holding any narratives about the folks you are helping that could adversely impact your leadership and/or their experience? If so why and how can you relinquish or resolve those judgements or narratives?

CONNECT WITH THE FOLKS YOU'RE HELPING

What can you see in the material that uniquely connects to the their story? What questions might be helpful to ask based on that?

Where can you anticipate the discussion might get challenging and how can you prepare for that?

#3   BIG PICTURE

KEY POINTS FOR THIS SECTION

The tips/tools/tactics presented here are an opportunity to adopt behaviors that are trust building by being trustworthy.

All of these tactics are reasonable; some require more effort and sacrifice than others, but all are feasible.

Willingness matters. The more difficult to implement, the more potential trust building mileage.

WHAT TO WATCH FOR / BE AWARE OF

FOR HUSBANDS

- Minimizing, arrogance and/or pride showing up as excuses or defenses to not adopt these tools.

- A lack of heart to engage the tips/tools/tactics because they require time and committed consistency.

FOR WIVES

- Reminding wives that healthy detachment and allowing him to either do the work or not is good.

- It's ok to ask questions to gain emotional safety. No question is off limits.

- Some of the tactical is trial and error. Some things will hit the mark, others won't and that is ok. One size does not fit all in the process.

08

OTHER WAYS WE CAN HELP

HELP FOR MEN

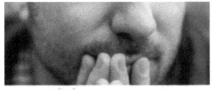

EMPATHY MASTERCLASS

HELP WITH CULTIVATING AND COMMUNICATING EMPATHY

Handling Her Triggers *MasterClass*

HOW TO HELP OUR WIVES HEAL WHEN THEY ARE TRIGGERED

When our wives are triggered it can feel like *a tidal wave of emotion*

WWW.REDEMPTIVELIVING.COM/MASTERCLASS

HELP FOR MEN

HELPING YOU ENGAGE
INTIMACY INSTEAD OF
RUNNING FROM IT

MOVING RECOVERY
FORWARD WHEN WE
ARE STUCK

WWW.REDEMPTIVELIVING.COM/MASTERCLASS

HELP FOR COUPLES

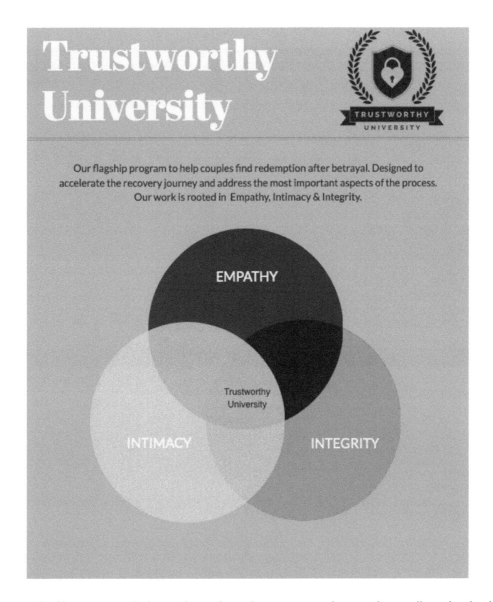

Trustworthy University includes traditional coaching sessions, live teaching calls and individual accountability calls for husbands. It is designed to expedite the recovery process for couples and aims at the best outcome possible - redemption!

WWW.REDEMPTIVELIVING.COM/TRUSTWORTHYUNIVERSITY

HELP FOR COUPLES

OUR VIDEO COURSE FOR COUPLES WHERE SHELLEY AND JASON TALK THROUGH EVERYTHING FROM PREPARING FOR DISCLOSURE TO WALKING IN REDEMPTION.

WWW.KITCHENCONVOS.COM

HELP FOR COUPLES

OUR PODCAST WHERE WE TALK ABOUT THE MOST
CHALLENGING AND REWARDING PARTS OF THE JOURNEY
IN A WELCOMING WAY.

WHEREVER YOU PREFER TO LISTEN!

HELP FOR WIVES

SHELLEY AND THE COACHES ON HER TEAM CARE FOR WIVES, EQUIP THEM FOR THE PROCESS AND PROVIDE A SAFE COMMUNITY.

SUPPORT GROUPS

Led by women who have lived it, these groups create community and utilize the Rescued workbook.

INDIVIDUAL COACHING

1 on 1 coaching to help you through the nuances of your journey.

ON-LINE COURSES

Learn at your own pace, in the privacy of your own home.

WWW.RLFORWOMEN.COM

BOOKS

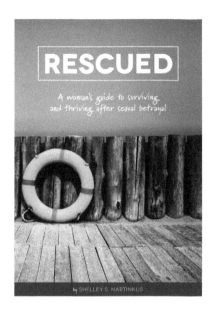

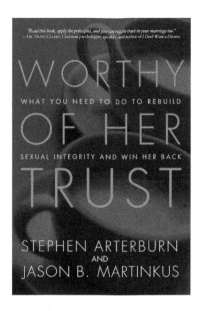

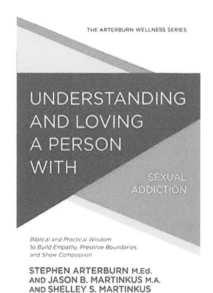

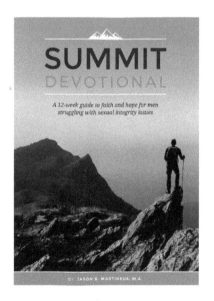

BOOKS CAN BE PURCHASED THROUGH OUR WEBSITES OR
AT AMAZON.COM

WWW.REDEMPTIVELIVING.COM
WWW.RLFORWOMEN.COM

THANK YOU!

It's not just about the outcome. It's about who we become.

THANK YOU!

Thank you for allowing us to walk a little of the journey with you. It truly is a privilege and not something taken lightly. Our sincere hope is that something in the material moves you forward in the process or, at the very least, helps you avoid a few mistakes and saves both of you some of the heartache.

This is a tough journey. Throughout this curriculum/course we've tried to keep instilling hope that trust and redemption are possible! We believe it's possible because we have the power of heaven on our side, and a God who is still in the business of redemption in the lives of His people. Not just for eternity, but even in the here-and-now.

So often in Scripture, especially in the old testament, the path to redemption for God's people went through challenge and struggle. Whether opposing nations, in-fighting, giants or angry kings, rarely was the good thing on the other side handed to them. They had to seize it. Walk toward it. Fight for it. Pray for it. In some cases even lay down their life for it.

Our journey is no different. Redemption won't be a hand-out.

But it will be worth it.

Not just because of the outcome, but because of who we become. Those battles, tests, trials and tribulations shaped God's people. They were walking into His redemption changed. We even wonder, in our own journeys, if God had simply taken away the struggle and given us a great marriage if it wouldn't have crumbled anyway. Because we woudn't have become more mature in character and sanctification. We would've been the same men, only without the same struggle. We would not have been responsible or resilient enough to be a good steward of the gift God was giving us.

For husbands, our hope is that you will focus on who you'll be if you let God change you, not on what you'll get if you change. Let yourself be moldable and malleable. Be formed into His image. Allow the refinement of this process to be about more than not acting out or betrayal. Allow it to be about reflecting God's glory and goodness.

For wives, we encourage you to be patient. Ugh. But it's true. You don't know who you might get on the other side of all this. Or what kind of marriage you'll have. And you don't necessarily yet know what God might be doing in you. We believe He has good for you, even in the middle of so much bad. Remember that people can't judge you for staying or leaving. That's between you and God. And you are courageous for getting this far.

Printed in the USA
CPSIA information can be obtained
at www.ICGtesting.com
CBHW080231111223
2358CB00013B/3

9 780578 970349